THE DAY OF THE
DINOSAUR

John Man

THE DAY OF T

HE DINOSAUR

John Man

BISON BOOKS

Copyright © 1978 Bison Books Limited
All rights reserved
ISBN 0 86124 003 0
Printed in Hong Kong
Published by Bison Books Limited,
4 Cromwell Place, London SW7
Printed in Hong Kong
ISBN 0 86124 003 0

Editor: John Man
Designer: Roy Williams
Picture Research: Linda Proud

Contents

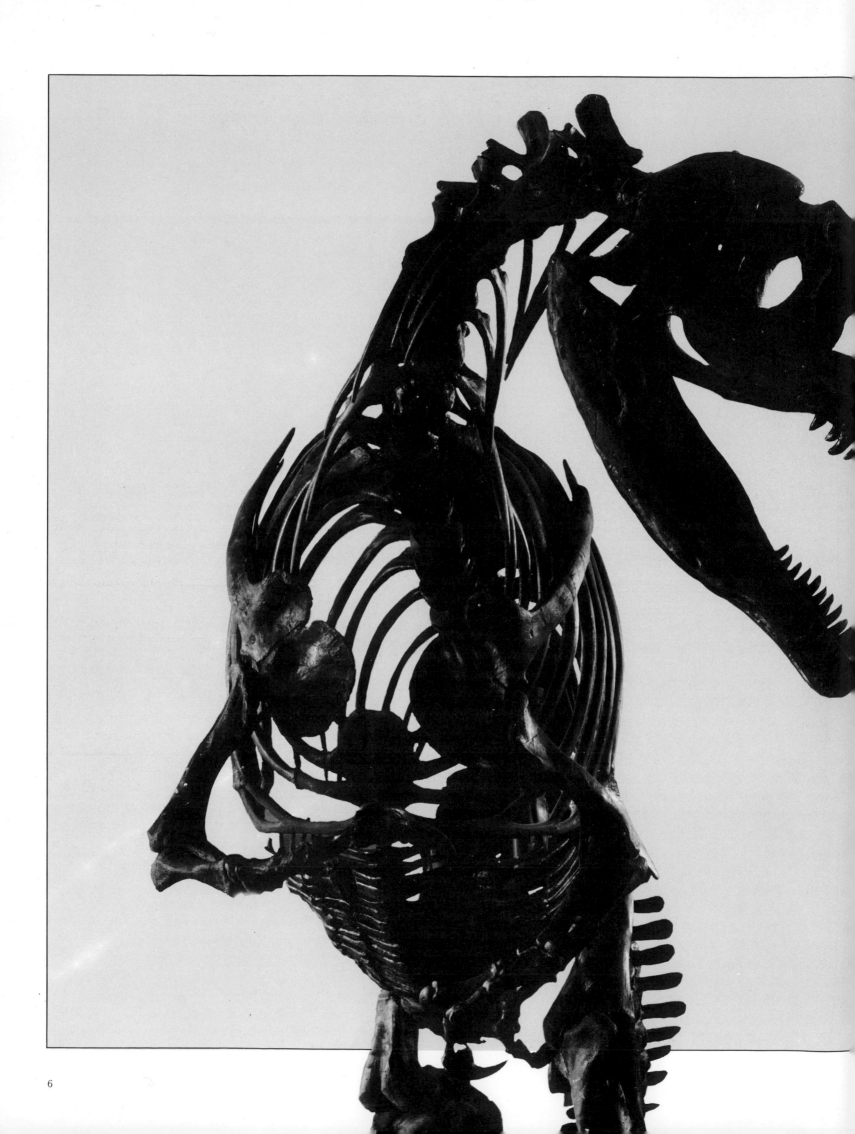

Introduction

Every child knows about dinosaurs. Countless six-year-olds across the Western world can point out a *Brontosaurus, Stegosaurus* or *Tyrannosaurus*. The complexity of the names does not bother them. They take as much pleasure in the names as in the power of the creatures themselves. Their knowledge often strikes their parents as incongruously precocious.

But that is usually as far as it gets. On this subject, parents seldom know much more than their children. Most people acquire little more than an attitude towards the creatures – an image of vast, cumbersome brutes, sometimes fierce, perhaps weighed down with armor, certainly stupid and conservative, heading towards inevitable extinction, displaced by the agile, intelligent, adaptable mammals that led to man.

Even this perhaps goes a little beyond the knowledge of many people. The time scales involved are incomprehensibly vast and experts are used to members of the public assuming that dinosaurs terrorized a world inhabited by cave-men, a view endorsed by countless monster movies in which a terror-stricken, scantily-clad Raquel Welch figure retreats backwards from a voracious *Tyrannosaurus*. Cartoonists, too, delight in showing dinosaurs and men in association. How many thousands of people believe that cave-men lived cheek-by-jowl with dinosaurs purely as a result of watching the TV program, *The Flintstones?*

The plain fact is that dinosaurs need a new deal. Their image does them little justice and beliefs about them are all too often just plain wrong.

For one thing the dinosaurs were all extinct some 60 million years before even the most primitive of men made his appearance on the earth. Man's fossil record extends back perhaps four million years. The dinosaurs when they became extinct had been on the earth for about 140 million years. Only after they vanished did the mammals get their chance. The dinosaurs and their related groups of reptiles thus dominated the earth for at least twice as long as the mammals have been around. The mammals as a whole – let alone our own species, *Homo sapiens* – will have to last another 80 million years to qualify as an equal success.

Moreover the dinosaurs dominated the land as the mammals do now and they were as varied in their life styles as the mammals are. Many hundreds of tons of dinosaur fossils have revealed that there were several hundred species, ranging from creatures not much bigger than chickens up to the more familiar 80-ton giants. Indeed, because the dinosaurs can be known only from their fossil record – the scattered remnants that by some rare coincidence become trapped in the right sort of sediments and turn to stone – there must be scores of other species yet to be discovered. There must also be scores more, no parts of which were fossilized; of these, we shall never know anything.

Slow? Cumbersome? Ill-equipped for survival? No, indeed. Many species were adapted for rapid and sustained action on their hind legs. Even the giants were beautifully engineered to cope with their massive bulk on dry land. Some recent reconstructions of *Diplodocus*, the largest of the dinosaurs, at almost 90 feet, show it as quite capable of galloping giraffe-like across the ancient plains.

The implications of such adaptations are dramatic, and as a result, a number of paleontologists have found themselves involved in scientific controversy as never before. As Robert Bakker wrote in a 1975 Scientific American article suitably entitled *Dinosaur Renaissance*, 'recent research is rewriting the dinosaur dossier.'

Among the major issues are:
   - were the dinosaurs 'reptiles' as we now know the term? Or were they as efficient in their physiology as mammals? Could they run fast, and for long periods? Were they, in fact, 'hot-blooded' as opposed to 'cold-blooded'? If so, when did this fortunate trait evolve?
   - if they were so successful, why should they have died out, leaving the earth to the apparently insignificant mammals that had inhabited the earth for the previous 200 million years – minute shrew-like creatures scampering, climbing or burrowing to safety at the approach of huge reptilian feet?
   - when dinosaurs were first discovered, many scientists noted that those that walked on their back legs had feet very like those of birds, many had hips surprisingly like birds and some were very similar to early birds in their skeletal structure. Could it be that birds are in fact nothing but minute versions of feathered dinosaurs?

The answers to these questions are by no means certain. But it is likely that the search for certainty will involve a drastic re-think of the way many groups of animals – both extinct and modern – are understood and classified.

The title of this book therefore has two senses. The first refers to the Age of the Dinosaurs which ended 65 million years ago. The extent of the fossil evidence now allows scientists to reconstruct the dinosaurs and their time with increasing accuracy – to summon them, in the words of a noted nineteenth-century researcher, 'from the abyss of time and from the depths of the earth.'

In a second sense, however, the title refers to the current revival of interest in the great beasts. In terms of scientific controversy, today is the Day of the Dinosaur.

This restoration of *Dilophosaurus*, a recent find from Arizona, represents the vivid way in which artists and scientists can together resurrect long extinct dinosaur species. The thin crests that run along the skull may have served as cooling devices or to distinguish the sexes.

Looming up in a glade at London's Crystal Palace, this 1854 reconstruction – the first – sees *Iguanodon* as quadrupedal not bipedal.

1/The Discovery of the Giants

I am standing on Boar's Hill, overlooking the university city of Oxford. In front of me, to the north, down the slope and beyond the main road that by-passes the city, extends a flood plain across which meanders the Thames on its way to London 60 miles to the east. They say that on very clear days one can see right across to the Bristol Channel, 70 miles westwards. I am slap in the middle of England. Oxford's spires dream away the afternoon (it is, in fact, one of the few views from which you can see more than two or three of the legendary 'dreaming spires'). In the distance I can see another hill, Shotover, and far off to my left across rolling pastures, beyond ancient woodlands, and stone-built villages, there is a hint of rising land: the beginning of the Cotswolds. It is a scene that seems, timelessly, to symbolize the very essence of rural England.

Yet it is not timeless; and once, very long ago, it was not in the least rural. Journey back in time, back before man ever came to Oxford 8000 years ago, back before *Homo* had evolved some four million years ago, even before the age of mammals began 60 million years ago – back 150 million years, before the Alps were formed, and when the Rockies were still plains.

At that time, Boar's Hill, Shotover and the Cotswolds did not exist. The rocks that make them were only then being laid down, for the whole area between Bristol and London was a vast, sheltered, shallow estuary.

Hover a moment, in your mind's eyes, above the sluggish waters. Look around you. The sea stretches to the southern horizon, unbroken by land. The world is, indeed, a very unfamiliar place. The continents are lumped together in two land masses. It will take them millennia yet to break apart and move towards their present positions. The estuary over which we are watching is a basin in the northern shores of a great ocean, the Tethys Sea. This spreads southward over what will one day be northern France, and down into the Mediterranean area. Then it rolls on both east and west, dividing the great land masses of the north and south.

Now look east. In the far distance, there is a streak on the horizon: land. Today London stands on its marshy verges. In your mind's eye zoom in on the shoreline. For several miles off shore, you will notice, the water is no more than a few feet deep, washing around clumps of water-plants. It is a foetid area, drying out occasionally in arid years. Palm-like trees and ferns line the water's edge, while further off, where the land begins to rise a little, there are conifers. The climate is muggy and the day windless. The lagoon teems with life. Fishes, crabs, shell-fish – many of which look familiar – thrive in the tropical waters. Dragonflies and beetles flap their way among the vegetation.

On the shore line, fronds shift and part to reveal the towering shape of what looks like a gigantic four-footed lizard. Its tiny head, on the end of its 15-foot neck, crops idly at the top of the trees. It is a *Cetiosaurus*, or 'whale-lizard,' one of the several species of giant herbivore that are established across the world. Smaller versions of the same creature amble after it – young who have temporarily left the herd to which the group belongs. The mother shoulders her ten-ton bulk out of the trees and on to the soggy shore, then warily pulls back as her elephantine feet squelch down into the mud. Instincts developed over millennia tell her of the dangers of becoming bogged in marshy ground, where she would fall easy prey to predators. She turns and moves easily back among the vegetation, followed by her young.

As the beasts vanish again into the thickets, a second, smaller creature emerges from the same clump of trees. It walks on its back legs its 15-foot tail held clear of the ground. Its serried rows of steak-knife teeth, set in two-foot jaws reveal it to be a flesh-eater. It is a megalosaur, an earlier and smaller version of the *Tyrannosaurus* that will, in millennia to come, be known as the most formidable land carnivore the world has ever seen.

This megalosaur, however, is not as formidable as it might be. It is ailing. Its days are clearly numbered. Instinct has impelled it in pursuit of the cetiosaurs that have now vanished again into the forest. But it could not have made a kill. It is too weak. It staggers down the beach, surprised by the sudden open ground and the soft slope. Its feet dig deep into the loose sand; it staggers to retain its balance, totters into the shallows, trips, and tumbles. Gulping and spluttering, it raises itself, and then falls again into deeper water. Several more times it struggles to regain the shore but fails. Eventually it subsides, its head beneath the lapping waves. After a few minutes, its heaving sides are still. Soon the body of the megalosaur has sunk into several inches of soft ooze and the water has almost completely covered it. The corpse is well away from land-based scavengers, and lies in water too shallow for the great flesh-eaters of the deep. Year by year – stripped now to bare bones – the skeleton is gradually swept towards deeper waters, along with the layers of sand and mud that bury it ever more deeply.

The scene is, of course, imaginary. Scientists cannot know for certain what happened on that remote occasion. But they can make a shrewd guess for the megalosaur was not alone – the estuary was the graveyard of countless animals, small and large. Over the centuries, many became fossilized in the sediments that coated the sea-bed.

Now move forward in time again, towards our starting point. The layers of material, compressed and buried in the shifting earth, changed over the millennia into slab-like sheets of rock. As the Oxford area assumed its present configuration, eons of rain and frost eroded the forming hills, and the lower layers of sedimentary rocks, uplifted and buckled, moved near the surface in several places. These processes proved of particular significance to science,

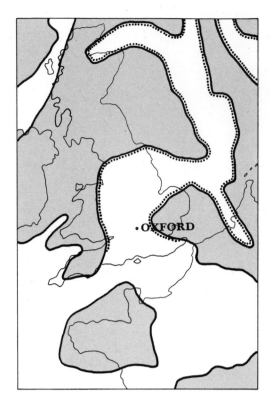

150 million years ago, much of north-western Europe was covered by a shallow, marshy inlet of the Tethys Ocean.

and to the residents of Oxfordshire – especially to the villagers of Stonesfield, ten miles to the north of the city.

In the seventeenth century, the slab-like rocks were found to make ideal roofing tiles. For more than 200 years, the mines of Stonesfield provided the local workmen with steady employment. The 'slate' (as it was called, although it was not technically slate but limestone and sandstone) was hacked out, allowed to split in the winter frosts into thinner sections, and then trimmed into tiles. In the course of their work, the miners had to handle every piece of rock and were familiar with the mass of fossilized creatures and plants contained within them. In the nineteenth century, when England was

The 12-inch fossil jaw-bone (right), still to be seen in the Oxford Museum, is part of the first dinosaur to be scientifically described – a *Megalosaurus* named by William Buckland in 1824. The fragment, half the length of the complete jaw, came from a creature similar to the one seen in the reconstruction (below). The teeth were scimitars of bone three or four inches long which were replaced continuously throughout the creature's life.

gripped by a positive fossil mania, the miners developed a lucrative side-line collecting fossils and selling them to tourists and dons.

Sometime in the first decade of the nineteenth century, a number of huge bones that were even then recognized as reptilian were delivered to Ashmolean Museum, Oxford. They were, in fact, the bones of our megalosaur, the first dinosaur to be given a name.

It was not, however, named at once. Although the discovery was to prove part of a revolution in the science of earth-history, there was as yet no framework within which these bones – and similar ones unearthed around the same time – could be understood. No one had any idea of the huge expanses of time to which we are nowadays accustomed. Almost everyone accepted that the earth had been created as recorded in the Book of Genesis. The vague Biblical time scale had even been specified with reassuring exactness by an Irish Archbishop, James Ussher, who in the seventeenth century announced that the earth had been created on Saturday 3 October 4004 BC at 8.00 in the evening. He worked out his figures by counting up the generations mentioned in the Old Testament. Only in the late eighteenth century – about 40 years before the first dinosaurian discoveries – did scientists begin to work out a more realistic chronology.

N°. 1. From the CREATION to the end of the XVIII. CENTURY Before CHRIST

Julian Period	Years before Christ	The Births, Deaths, Ages and Generations of the Patriarchs	Remarkable Events
710	4004	Adam created & ob. 3074 æt.930	4004 The Creation of the World *began according to Arch Bishop Usher on Sunday October 23 & in y.* *Year before the Vulgar Æra of the Birth of Christ as given in the* **Hebrew Text** .... 4004 In the **LXX** .... 5872 In the **Samaritan** .... 4700 *Adam & Eve were created on Friday October the 28. They are placed in Paradise, but are soon tempted & Fall; Sentence is pass'd upon them by God, who encourages them at the same time with the Promise of the Seed of the Woman. They are banish'd Paradise.* 4003 *The Birth of Cain, the first who was born of a Woman. Abel is born soon after.* 3875 *Abel is murder'd by Cain because his Sacrifice was more acceptable to God.* 3874 *Seth born, whose Offspring were call'd the Children of God by way of Distinction from those*

It became increasingly apparent that the buckled strata visible at any seaside – assumed by most people to be vestiges of the Creation itself – were in fact evidence of immense and slowly working forces in the earth. In 1785 James Hutton, in his *Theory of the Earth* set forth a belief that the forces that formed the earth were still at work. Wind and weather alone could, he said, if given sufficient time, produce every existing feature of the earth's crust. He concluded that the Biblical account of the Creation was a figment of the imagination. In studying the earth, he wrote, 'we find no vestige of a beginning – no prospect of an end.' It was clear that the time scale for the development of the earth could hardly be a mere 6000 years. It must at least be tens of thousands, if not hundreds of thousands, though few people yet dared to guess at a million or more.

This concept could account, in general terms, for the most problematical items found buried in the earth: fossils. A fossil was originally anything dug up but it soon became restricted in meaning to the remains, or indeed any product (like a footprint or burrow), of a living organism, animal or plant,

In a *Chronology and History of the World* of 1754, the date of the Creation still holds firmly to the time scale established by Archbishop James Ussher a hundred years previously. Geologists had already realized that such a minute time scale was insufficient to explain the processes of rock formation and mountain building, let alone the problems posed by fossil finds.

An Unwitting Record of a Dinosaur Relic

ROBERT PLOT, OXFORD'S 'CHEMISTRY' PROFESSOR

The first existing record of a dinosaur bone appeared in The Natural History of Oxfordshire, *published in 1677 by Robert Plot, Professor of 'Chymistry' at Oxford University. In his book, Plot describes a massive thigh-bone dug up at Cornwell Oxfordshire; it was almost certainly that of a megalosaur, though the bone itself vanished. Plot was of course unaware of the significance of the find, which he discusses in a chapter entitled 'Of Formed Stones.' In a later edition of his work, due to an editorial error, the fragment was wrongly labeled as a 'scrotum humanum' (human scrotum) — another type of 'formed stone' discussed by Plot. Even given the general belief in giants, to which Plot himself subscribed, it is hard to believe anyone taking seriously the idea of a man with a 20-pound scrotum, two feet around.*

'Next the *Stones* that relate to either of the three *Ventricles*, come we next to such as concern the *Artus*, or other *Members* of the *Body*: Amongst which, I have one dug out of a Quarry in the Parish of *Cornwell*, and given me by the Ingenious Sir *Thomas Pennyston*, that has exactly the Figure of the lowermost part of the *Thigh-Bone* of a *Man*, or at least of some other *Animal*, with the capital *Femoris inferiora*, between which are the *anterior* (hid behind the *sculpture*) and the larger *posterior Sinus*, the seat of the strong *Ligament* that rises out of the *Thigh*, and that gives safe passage to the *Vessels* descending into the *Leg*: And a little above the *Sinus*. where it seems to have been broken off, shewing the *Marrow* within of a shining *Spar-like* Substance, of its true Colour and Figure, in the *hollow* of the *Bone*. In Compass near the *capita Femoris* just two Foot, and at the Top above the *Sinus* (where the *Thigh-Bone* is as small as any where) about 15 Inches; in weight, though representing so short a part of the *Thigh-Bone*, almost 20 Pounds.

Which are *dimensions*, and a *weight*, so much exceeding the ordinary course of *Nature*, that by *Agricola*, *Caesalpinus*, and *Kircher*, such *Stones* have been rather thought to be Formed either in hollows of Rocks . . . or by some other sportive *plastic Power* of the Earth . . .

And that indeed there are *Stones* thus naturally fashioned must be no means be doubted, . . . [but] none of them, as the judicious *Charles* Marquess of *Ventimiglia* well observed, having any *signs* of *hollowness* for the place of the *Marrow*. . . .

Which has fully convinced me that this *Stone* of ours was not so produced, it having those *Signs* exquisitely expressed; but must have been a real *Bone*, now Petrified . . . . . it must have belong'd to some greater *Animal* than either an *Ox* or *Horse*; and if so (say almost all other *Authors* in the like Case) in probability it must have been the *Bone* of some *Elephant*, brought hither during the Government of the *Romans* in Britain: But this Opinion too lies under so great Difficulties, that it can hardly be admitted; which are briefly these.

First, That we do not find that any of the *Roman Authors*, who elsewhere are large enough in describing the *Elephant's* behaviour in *Fight*, and how terrible they were to some of the *Trans-Alpine* Nations, mention any such matter in any of their *Expeditions* into *Britain*. . . .

Beside, had this *Thigh-bone* and *Tooth* [which was found together with the thigh-bone] . . . been ever the Spoils of *Elephants*, we should certainly at some time or other have met also with those greater *Tusks* with which they are armed, of which I have not heard there have been any yet found in *England*, nor any thing like them.

And hereunto, what prevails with me much, that since the great Conflagration of *London*, Anno 1666. upon the pulling down of St. *Mary Wool-Church*, and making the Site of it into a *Market-place*, there was found a *Thigh-bone* (supposed to be of a *Woman*) which was to be seen at the *King's -Head Tavern* at *Greenwich* in *Kent*, much bigger and longer than ours of *Stone*, could in proportion be, had it been entire. We have also here at *Oxford*, a *Thigh-bone* that came from *London*, three Foot and two Inches long, which I guess may be of an agreeable proportion with ours. And the same Day I brought the Tooth from *Cornwell*, there were two others happily procured for me by my worthy Friend *Samuel Fowler*, dug up in the Parish Church of *Morton-Valence*, about seven Miles from *Glocester*, in the way thence to *Bristol*, in all points so exactly like the other from *Cornwell*, in Ridges, Cavities, etc. that had they not differ'd somewhat in Colour, they could scarce have any way been distinguish'd. Now how *Elephants* should come to be buried in *Churches*, is a Question not easily answered, except we will run to so groundless a shift, as to say, that possibly the *Elephants* might be there buried before *Christianity* flourish'd in Britain. . . .

But what is *instar omnium* in this difficult point, there happily came to *Oxford* while I was writing of this, a living Elephant to be shewn publickly at the ACT, *An.* 1676. with whose *Bones* and *Teeth* I compared ours; and found those of the *Elephant* not only of a different Shape, but also incomparably bigger than *ours*, though the Beast were very young and not half grown. If then they are neither the Bones of *Horses*, *Oxen*, nor *Elephants*, as I am strongly perswaded they are not, upon Comparison, and from their like found in *Churches*: It remains, that (notwithstanding their extravagant Magnitude) they must have been the Bones of *Men* or *Women*.'

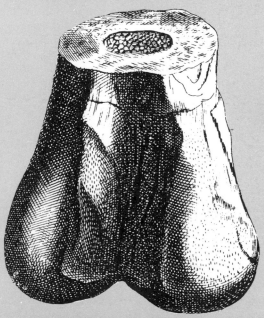

THE ENIGMATIC THIGH-BONE

which had been turned to stone. When a dead organism is buried in sediment, the soft parts decay but the hard parts – the bones – remain for longer. Sometimes water, bearing minerals, filters through the bones; gradually the minerals replace the old organic structure. The bone literally becomes rock but of a form slightly different from that which surrounds it. From time immemorial, men have recognized many fossils as the remains of animals. But could the existence of such objects be reconciled with the Biblical account of the Creation?

There were explanations, though they seem singularly bad ones today. Some people said there was a force in nature called the *vis plastica*, a 'forming force' that created rocks to look like organisms; others that fossils represented animals that were imperfect prototypes of existing animals; yet others that fossils were the Devil's work, put there to deceive men. But the most popular idea was that all creatures and plants found fossilized had been drowned in the Flood (though even for a fundamentalist Christian, the idea scarcely bears deep consideration. Noah was supposed to have taken a pair of every beast into the Ark; how then to explain the fact that some species were clearly extinct? And what of the rest of the human race, supposedly destroyed for their transgressions, not a single fossilized relic of whom had been found?)

The discovery that there had once existed whole races of massive creatures, not a living trace of which now survived, was part of the revolution that culminated in the acceptance of Darwin's theory of evolution in the second half of the century. In this revolution fact and theory had to march hand in hand. It was the same with the recognition of the dinosaurs: fact alone – in this case the discovery of bones – was not enough.

Indeed dinosaur bones must have been found countless times and discarded, or explained away. A case in point: in 1676 Oxford's inquisitive Professor of 'Chymistry,' Dr Robert Plot, wrote his *Natural History of Oxfordshire* and included – all unknowingly – the earliest known record of a dinosaur bone, probably also that of a megalosaur. The bone, which came from a graveyard, 'has exactly the figure of the lowermost part of the thigh bone of a man, or at least some other animal' – except that the whole thigh-bone must have been several feet long. The doctor wondered idly whether it was the bone of an elephant but pointed out that a quick comparison with an elephant – one was fortunately put on show in Oxford at about the time he was writing his book – showed that the bone could not have belonged to that species. It was too small. Plot concluded that the bone was that of a giant human. There are other references over the centuries to enormous bones dug up out of the earth but the problems they posed were only solved with the description of the Stonesfield megalosaur.

There has long been some debate about who named the first dinosaur. Pride of place usually goes to a south coast doctor, Gideon Mantell, who identified the teeth of an *Iguanodon*, a large, bipedal plant-eater. He published details of these findings in 1825. But by then the more extensive collection of megalosaur bones had been known for several years, in particular to one of the most extraordinary of Oxford's many extraordinary characters, William Buckland. Buckland was a delightful eccentric. Outgoing and curious he was also brilliant, a man both of religion and of science, who combined two careers and many interests, notably those of geology and paleontology. He took Holy Orders at Oxford but his passion for chemistry, mineralogy and geology took over in his twenties, and at the age of 29, in 1813, he was appointed Reader in Mineralogy at Oxford. Six years later, he became the first Professor of Geology, and later still was appointed Dean of St Paul's in London.

His eccentricities were legion. His umbrella was engraved: 'stolen from Dr Buckland.' His house at Christ Church was a mass of bones, live animals and pieces of rock. Buckland claimed to have eaten his way through the entire animal kingdom – the most unpleasant meal being vole and the next most unpleasant bluebottle. He kept a bear with the extraordinary name Tiglath Pileser (the name of a king of ancient Babylon). 'Tig,' as he was affectionately known, appeared at the 1847 meeting of the British Association for the Advancement of Science in Oxford, one of whose members mesmerized the bear until it fell unconscious on the ground. One visitor to Buckland described how his interview was conducted to the sounds of a jackal crunching up guinea-pigs under the sofa.

GIDEON MANTELL   MARY ANN MANTELL

The bones that seized Buckland's passing interest around 1820 were already well known in scientific circles. They consisted of a jaw bone, a thigh bone, ribs, scapulae, vertebrae, and had been seen – among others – by the great Baron Georges Cuvier of Paris, founder of the science of comparative anatomy, whose words in matter of fossil identification were regarded as almost divine. Cuvier mentions having seen the bones while on a visit to Buckland in 1818, and in 1820 a friend of Buckland's wrote to him about his 'Stonesfield reptile.' Eventually on 20 February 1824, Buckland got around to reading a description of the bones to the Geological Society of London. His paper was called *Notice on the Megalosaurus, or Great Fossil Lizard, of Stonesfield*. He identified the creature as a Saurian, or lizard, and said that the bones suggested an animal of 40 feet long with the bulk of an elephant, seven feet high. The bones are still in the Oxford Museum. The name Buckland adopted at the suggestion of a friend and fellow geologist, the Rev W Conybeare. It was apt enough: *Megalosaurus* simply means 'giant lizard.' Buckland had, of course, no inkling of the true significance of his find but his paper is the first scientific description of a dinosaur.

Mantell's major claim to fame lies in the fact that he was the first to name a dinosaur bone that he had found himself. Doctoring was only Mantell's

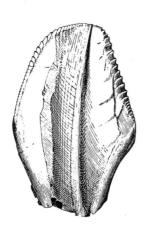

AN IGUANODON TOOTH

second interest. His first passion was fossils. It was a passion that grew in him early. He was born in 1790 in Lewes, not far from the south coast resort of Brighton. As a boy he used to wander through the countryside exploring the quarries and river banks where the rain and streams washed countless fossils out of the local sedimentary rocks. In 1816 he married a good-looking young woman, Mary Ann Woodhouse, and two years later bought a fine house in Lewes. Simultaneously he began work on his monumental *The Fossils of the South Downs*. He infected Mary Ann with his passion – indeed she would have been hard pressed to escape from it – and she began to prepare the several hundred drawings that were to illustrate his book. Whenever Mantell – often accompanied by his wife – went out into the countryside to see a patient, he kept a sharp eye open for fossils.

One day early in 1822, the Mantells were visiting a patient near Cuckfield, Sussex, and while Gideon went inside, Mary Ann took a stroll along the road. In a pile of stones to be used for filling in the ruts and potholes in the road, Mrs

THE COAT OF ARMS OF MAIDSTONE, KENT

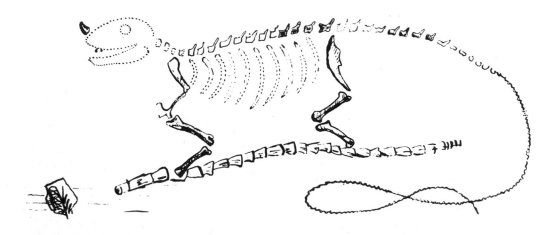

The *Iguanodon* ('iguana-tooth') was originally named for the resemblance between its teeth and those of the iguana (left). Mantell, in his first reconstruction of his discovery (above), took the resemblance further and imagined it as a tree-dwelling quadruped.

A Jewel-Case of Fossils

The word 'fossil' has a dry-as-dust ring to it, yet fossils may also be delicate, varied and of rare beauty. Indeed, it is from tiny, jewel-like objects, like the ones shown here, that paleontologists can often best reconstruct the world in which long extinct animals lived. Often more tellingly than the bones of massive animals, the delicate tracery of a leaf, a diminutive sea creature or an insect embalmed in a drop of tree gum can evoke the color and life of vanished ages.

A TRILOBITE

A FISH *EUBIODECTAS LIBANICUS*

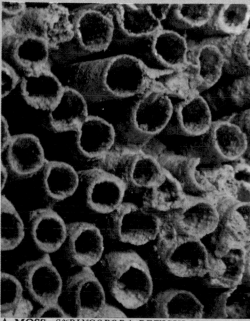

A MOSS *SYRINGOPORA RETICULATA*

LEAF OF A CINNAMON TREE

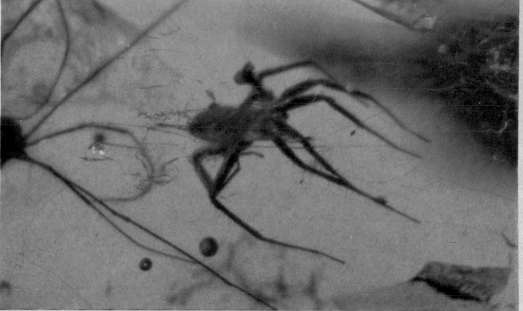

SPIDER IN AMBER

Mantell's eye was caught by something glinting. She walked over and picked it up. It was a rock that contained a fossil tooth – one of a kind she had never seen before. Naturally she took it back with her to the carriage and showed her husband when he returned from his patient. It was, Gideon recorded later, 'a large tooth which, from the worn, smooth and oblique surface of the crown had evidently belonged to an herbivorous animal' but he could not identify it further.

He made some enquiries and found that the rock in which the tooth was implanted had come from a local quarry. He acquired other similar teeth. The strata in which they had been found were of what we now call Cretaceous age. It was a puzzle. No herbivorous reptiles were known at the time and no mammals had ever been found in such ancient strata.

Hoping to solve the riddle, Mantell showed the bones to a number of friends. He was told rather discouragingly that the teeth were of no particular interest, that they belonged to some large fish, or were merely mammal's teeth that had been washed into deceptively ancient strata. He asked a friend of his, Charles Lyell, soon to be England's most eminent geologist, to take a tooth to France to be viewed by the great Cuvier himself. Cuvier dismissed the tooth as that of a rhinoceros and, when Mantell later sent him some ankle bones from the same quarry, Cuvier identified them as belonging to a species

Paleontologist and workers chip at stones in the Cuckfield, Sussex, quarry that in 1822 yielded the first relics of *Iguanodon*. The quarry was filled in a few years later.

of hippopotamus. A small pointed bone was a particular puzzle: it was identified by other experts as a rhinoceros horn.

Mantell decided to continue the research himself. He was certain the bones were of interest, he was certain they really did come from the Cretaceous strata and was determined to solve the puzzle on his own. He felt sure the bones were not those of a mammal living or extinct and concluded, therefore, that they might be the bones of an extinct reptile, even though very few reptiles were known to include plants in their diet. He clearly felt himself on the verge of a great discovery.

He took the bones and teeth to London to work in the Hunterian Museum at the Royal College of Surgeons, which had the best collection of bones, both human and animal, in the country. There, for a day, he sifted through drawer after drawer containing reptilian bones and teeth but found nothing similar to his own specimen. Fortunately a young man by the name of Samuel Stutchbury, a naturalist with a knowledge of South American animals, was also working in the Museum on the same day. Stutchbury saw Mantell's teeth and at once spotted a resemblance between them and those of an iguana, a six-foot tropical American lizard that is largely herbivorous.

He showed Mantell an iguana tooth and Mantell saw that his own fossil was very similar – except that it was many times larger. This was good enough for Mantell. He coined a name for his new creature, *Iguanosaurus*, but at the suggestion of Buckland's friend, Conybeare (who thus deserves some recognition for inventing the names of the first two known dinosaurs) decided to call it by the shorter, more euphonious and indeed more accurate *Iguanodon* – 'iguana tooth.'

Mantell wrote again to Cuvier in triumph. Cuvier's response was gratifying: 'these teeth are certainly unknown to me,' he said, and then confirmed Mantell's own thinking: 'Might we not have here a new animal, an herviborous reptile?' On 10 February 1825, Mantell's full account of his

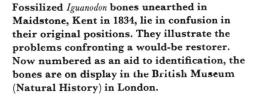

Fossilized *Iguanodon* bones unearthed in Maidstone, Kent in 1834, lie in confusion in their original positions. They illustrate the problems confronting a would-be restorer. Now numbered as an aid to identification, the bones are on display in the British Museum (Natural History) in London.

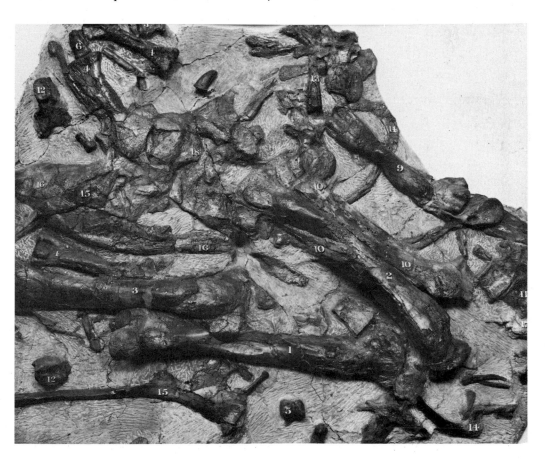

discovery was presented to the Royal Society.

In the next 15 years, several other bones were found and identified as those of extinct reptiles. One particularly fine example again concerned Mantell. In 1834 a partial skeleton of an *Iguanodon* was found at Maidstone in Kent, in a quarry owned by a man named W H Bensted. Bensted was fortunately something of a local intellectual and 'at once perceived that it was a fossil bone belonging to an animal of great magnitude.' Bensted erected a shelter over the bones, already blasted clear by gunpowder, and set about chipping them out from the surrounding rock. Keen to identify his find he wrote directly to Mantell, who journeyed to Maidstone and recorded in his diary 'they are the lower extremities of an *Iguanodon*; a magnificent group, visited the quarry where they were dug up; went to bed very late.' Mantell offered £10 for the find but Bensted wanted £25; the money was raised by some friends of Mantell who presented him with the block of fossils. A century later, in commemoration of the find, the *Iguanodon* became part of the Maidstone coat-of-arms, which now – according to the ringing official description – contains 'on the dexter side an *Iguanodon* proper, collared.'

Mantell's work on the *Iguanodon* marked the high point of his life. He described another great reptile, *Hylaeosaurus*, in 1832 but could not make a living from fossils. His practice never prospered and the strains that his part-time passion imposed on his marriage proved too much for Mary Ann. In 1838 he sold his collection to the British Museum for £4000. The following year, Mary Ann and his children left, elbowed out of his life as it were, by the *Iguanodon*. In 1841 Mantell injured his spine in a carriage accident and never fully recovered. He died ten years later, morose and introverted.

There were other discoveries, as well, hinting at the true wealth of extinct reptiles yet to be assessed. In his notice on the *Megalosaurus*, Buckland referred to 'the bones of large cetaceous (i.e. whale-like) animals,' found to the north of Oxford. The fragments, when reassembled, formed a thigh-bone four foot

Underground in a Maastricht, Holland, quarry a German doctor, Hoffman, supervises the removal of a slab of rock containing the fossilized jaws of a mosasaur. Found in 1770 and identified as the remains of a sea-going, lizard-like creature, the mosasaur jaws planted the idea that there had once existed races of vast reptilians, now long extinct.

Mary Anning, Fossil-Hunter Extraordinary

Nearly all the fossil finds of ancient reptiles in the nineteenth-century were made by amateurs. The most exceptional of them was Mary Anning, of Lyme Regis, on England's south-west coast. Her flair was later ascribed by one biographer to a strange incident: when she was one, she and her nurse were struck by lightning. The nurse was killed but little Mary was revived with a hot bath. 'She had been a dull child before,' ran the story 'but after this accident became lively and intelligent.'

Mary's father was a carpenter who collected fossils on the side, taking his daughter with him on daily walks along the fossil-rich Blue Lias cliffs of the area. He died when she was ten but she continued collecting. The following year she found an ichthyosaur and even hired a team of men to help her extract the bones. She later became the first person to discover a complete plesiosaur fossil and the first to find a pterodactyl in Great Britain. It was said that one of her greatest discoveries was made when she climbed on to a rock, looked down and saw she was standing on the fossilized skull of a reptile.

Though no scientist, she became such an expert on fossils, which she sold for a living, that the most eminent geologists of the day sought her friendship. Fittingly her portrait (above) – showing a comfortably proportioned middle-aged lady carrying a geologist's hammer and a specimen basket and accompanied by her black-and-white dog – now hangs in the British Museum (Natural History).

three inches long, which made it the largest fossil bone then known. This, carefully cemented and bound round with wire, is still to be seen in the Oxford Museum. Other bones of the same creature, later named *Cetiosaurus oxoniensis*, were found at nearby villages. Buckland was well aware that all these bones belonged to a single hitherto undescribed type of large reptile. The fragments were indications of what was to come in the second half of the century, for they were in fact the first known bones of the largest of the dinosaurs, the sauropods – the massive, heavy-limbed long-necked, long-tailed, small-headed quadrupeds that are, in the popular imagination, the very epitome of the dinosaur.

By now it had also become apparent that these great lizards – if lizards they were – had not been restricted to the land. In 1770 chalk quarry workers at Maastricht, Holland, found the jaws of a huge marine animal. This find has a story all of its own. A local collector, Dr Hoffmann, who was a retired German military surgeon, was sought out to identify the find. Hastily Hoffmann had the workmen hew out the jaws and returned home with them. The fame of the four-foot jaw soon reached a local canon named Godin. Godin owned the land above the quarry and on this basis he claimed the jaws for himself, sued Hoffman, won, and took possession of the fossil.

In 1795 the town was besieged by the Republican French Army. The commander of the besieging troops, General Pichegru, had also heard of the jaws and directed his artillery not to hit the museum in which the fossil lay. Godin noticed this, astutely guessed the reason and hid the jaws elsewhere. When the town fell, and Pichegru found the museum empty of the find, he offered 600 bottles of wine for its retrieval – a prize claimed in a remarkably short time by a bevy of French officers. Back in France, the jaws were examined by Cuvier himself, who described them correctly as those of an extinct lizard, although the creature was named only in 1828 – again by Conybeare – who called it *Mosasaurus*, after the Meuse River near which it was found.

In the early nineteenth century other 'lizards' were found in England, many by Mary Anning. She lived in the English south coast town of Lyme Regis, where fossils were particularly common. Her father, who had been a carpenter, used to make some money on the side by picking up the remains of ancient fossil seashells and selling them, a task in which she helped him. In 1811, when she was just 12-years-old, working with her rock hammer, she exposed the bones of what she thought to be an unusual species of crocodile. It was in fact the first skeleton of an ichthyosaur or 'fish reptile' which became widely known.

She had, as it happened, an unerring instinct for brilliant fossil finds; in 1824 she found one of the first, complete plesiosaurs and in 1828 one of the earliest examples of a pterosaur or 'winged lizard.'

By 1841 nine separate species of these extinct reptile-like creatures had been found. How were they to be explained and understood? The first man to set them all on a proper scientific footing – to regard them not as several individual problems but as different aspects of one great problem – was Richard Owen. Owen trained in medicine but became interested in anatomical research, and in 1836, aged only 32, he became a Professor at the Royal College of Surgeons. Owen was to become England's greatest anatomist, the 'English Cuvier,' and it was largely through his initiative and insight that the British Museum (Natural History) was later established. Owen made a close study of the bones of *Megalosaurus*, *Iguanodon* and *Hylaeosaurus* and was convinced that they were not the bones of ancient lizards, or crocodiles, or any other reptiles of the kinds that inhabit the world today. They were, he argued, something completely different and should be regarded as a group of their own.

In 1841 he read his lengthy, detailed *Report on British Fossil Reptiles* to the British Association. In the second part of this he suggested that the new finds, which possessed characteristics 'manifested by creatures far surpassing in size the largest of existing reptiles,' be regarded as representatives of 'a distinct tribe or suborder of Saurian Reptiles for which I would propose the name *Dinosauria*,' which in a footnote he defines as '*deinos* – fearfully great; *sauros* – a lizard.' Thus Owen added a new word to the English language and created the popular image of an earth inhabited by the most massive land animals that have ever existed. It was, in some ways, an unfortunate image, for it soon became apparent that the dinosaurs were not all equally closely related and it would have been better, zoologically, not to have grouped them together. But the image stuck and the imagination – if not the phylogenetic awareness – of the general public was much enriched.

Owen had rather special reasons for wishing to create the 'tribe' Dinosauria and for bringing its members so powerfully to life. In the great debate on evolution that was to reach its peak in the second half of the century after the publication of Darwin's *Origin of Species* in 1859, Owen was on the side of the traditionalists. A powerful current in orthodox scientific and religious thinking held that species were immutable, the direct result of God's work. Extinct species, as represented in the fossil record, were explained by an extension of the Flood theory – the species had perished in periodic catastrophes that wiped out much or all of animal life. According to this view, man and his contemporary creatures were the result of the last 'Creation.'

This somewhat desperate notion was increasingly disputed by those who held that species evolved one from another over a period of time (a belief on which livestock breeders have always worked, even if they lacked any theoretical basis for their activities). Unfortunately for the evolutionists, no one succeeded in proposing a satisfactory mechanism by which such changes could have taken place. One scientist who tried was Jean Baptiste Lamarck, Cuvier's colleague in Paris, who believed that characteristics acquired by an individual during the course of its life could be passed on to its offspring and thus a species would be modified to accord to the life that many of its individuals led. How these modifications were actually passed on to the offspring, he could not, of course, explain.

Sir Richard Owen, who coined the word dinosaur, had a dedication to his fields – comparative anatomy and paleontology – and an oddly maniacal expression which combined to make him one of the best known scientists of his day.

To Owen such thinking was anathema. The ancient race of extinct reptiles that were now being dug up in many parts of Europe seemed to furnish him with the weapon that he needed to demolish Lamarck. He was determined to see the dinosaurs as a relatively 'advanced' race of reptiles. To claim that modern reptiles evolved from them would be to say that evolution had gone down hill. This was a contradiction in terms. In Owen's view there was only one possible alternative: that the dinosaurs and their relatives had been wiped out by some massive catastrophe and that animal life – including human life – had begun all over again.

To substantiate his views, he constructed an image of the dinosaurs' world. Assuming that they were reptilian and therefore 'cold-blooded' – that is, dependent on the heat of the sun to maintain their internal temperature – he supposed that the world as a whole was much warmer in their day. In addition he argued, the air must have been thicker then to support the flight of the clumsy, slow-moving pterodactyls. His vision was as philosophical and as speculative as Lamarck's but it had an immediate and lasting impact.

From Owen, we derive the image of a world populated by overblown lizards, slow-moving, often amphibious to support their massive bulk and stupid by comparison with the nimble, quick-witted mammals which succeeded them.

In many of his theories, Owen was too simplistic. There *were* mammals living in dinosaurian times. And modern reptiles – crocodiles and turtles for instance – are very ancient indeed, as ancient as the dinosaurs themselves. They are, in some respects, more 'primitive,' yet they survived when the dinosaurs became extinct: which, then, were 'superior'? Today Owen's simplistic image of the dinosaurs as nothing more than sluggish and ponderous lizards is still in great measure with us. It was at least unfair and – many would now argue – just plain wrong. But his theories achieved one thing: they created a framework within which other researchers could explore and reconstruct.

Owen's vision had such impact largely because it became a physical reality. When London's Great Exhibition of 1851 – held in Hyde Park to display the wonders of modern technology – closed, the glass vaults of the Crystal Palace which had housed the exhibition were dismantled and re-erected in the London suburb of Sydenham. Victoria's consort, Prince Albert, suggested that the new site be decorated with restored beasts of bygone ages. The man chosen for the task was a painter and sculptor, Benjamin Waterhouse Hawkins, who came upon Owen's papers about dinosaurs and determined to 'summon from the abyss of time and from the depths of the earth, those vast forms and gigantic beasts which the Almighty Creator designed with fitness to inhabit and precede us in possession of this part of the earth called Great Britain.'

On New Year's Eve 1853, Richard Owen at the 'head' of the table, toasts the near completion of the first dinosaur reconstruction – the *Iguanodon* that still stands in London's Crystal Palace gardens. A dozen or so guests sit within the cement-and-tile structure and other guests are accommodated round the rest of the T-shaped table which stretches away on the raised platform.

The Sad Fate of the Central Park Dinosaurs

In 1868 the Commissioners of New York's newly created Central Park, envious of England's Crystal Palace dinosaurs, determined to restore for the city 'the phenomena of the ancient epochs of this continent'. Clearly, there was only one man for the job – Benjamin Waterhouse Hawkins, the creator of the London reconstructions.

The park's comptroller, Andrew Green, wrote to Hawkins, offering him the contract. Hawkins accepted at once, and spent the summer and fall researching new fossil finds in Washington and Philadelphia. In December, he arrived in New York to begin work. To this end, he had a special studio built in the park's south-west corner.

Hawkins planned a lavish display, as his sketch (below) shows. There were to be hadrosaurs set upon by ferocious *Laelaps* (as the megalosaur-like *Dryptosaurus* was then known), plesiosaurs and mosasaurs lying in wait in pools, with various extinct mammalian giants in anachronistic attendance. All in all, it was intended – in the exaggerated words of the park's 1869 *Report* – to be 'a complete visual history of the American continent.'

The display was to be housed in a Paleozoic Museum, designed (like the Crystal Palace) with an iron frame and an arched roof of glass. Foundations were laid by Frederick Law Olmsted, the park's chief architect, in the park at Central Park West and 63rd Street.

Unfortunately for Hawkins, and indeed for the whole city, the scheme fell foul of New York's Byzantine and corrupt politics. In the 1860s the city was in the rapacious grasp of William Marcy Tweed, boss of the local Democratic Party and thus of the city's government. By such devices as padding payrolls and arranging cuts of city contracts, 'Boss' Tweed and his henchmen – the Tweed Ring – plundered New York of some $200 million between 1868 and 1871, when their rule was broken.

Tweed needed to establish control of every department to provide offices for his army of placemen. Central Park offered a fine opportunity for him to extend his power. His right-hand men, Peter 'Brains' Sweeny, formed an all-embracing Department of Public Parks and ousted Green from office. In early 1871, seeing no financial gain to be had from the Paleozoic Museum, Sweeny killed the project.

Hawkins, meanwhile, had finished at least seven of his models. One day in spring, 1871, vandals hired by Sweeny burst into his studio, smashed the models and their casts with sledge-hammers and buried the pieces in the park.

Hawkins, distraught, went to Princeton, where he completed a number of paintings which show, with considerable verve, his views of the creatures he had tried vainly to reconstruct. He even built one more model, a hadrosaur, to celebrate the centenary of the Declaration of Independence in 1876. It was shown in Philadelphia and Washington, where, apparently it was allowed to weather away.

Hawkins' Paleozoic Museum as it should have looked. At left *Laelaps* attacks a *Hadrosaurus*, at center two *Laelaps* squabble over a corpse.

In Hawkins' painting, predatory *Laelaps* (now renamed *Dryptosaurus*), hadrosaurs and mosasaurs dominate a Cretaceous scene set in New Jersey.

Clearly modeled on a lion, a sinister *Megalosaurus bucklandi*, wrongly portrayed as a quadruped, guards its newly-killed prey.

With Owen's help, Hawkins restored *Iguanodon*, *Hylaeosaurus* and *Megalosaurus*, placing them on all fours like rhinoceroses. *Iguanodon's* horn-like appendage – which we now know is its thumb – was placed upon its nose to reinforce the rhinoceros image. Numerous other life-size models of other extinct animals – ichthyosaurs, plesiosaurs, extinct mammals, ancient amphibians and crocodiles – were made by Hawkins under Owen's direction and scattered among the trees and shrubbery, where they still stand to this day. In an often retold incident Hawkins and Owen celebrated the imminent end to their work by holding a dinner inside the near-complete model of the *Iguanodon* – a massive creation of 600 bricks and some 1500 tiles.

This venture has an odd postscript. Twenty years later the indefatigable Hawkins tried a repeat performance in New York's Central Park. The attempt was shattered (literally) in an assault that was a by-product of the city's violent Byzantine politics.

LOUIS DOLLO

The work of the early dinosaur hunters and theorists had introduced a new race of creatures to the world. They could do little more than that, however, because the evidence of how many types of dinosaur there were, what they looked like and how they lived was remarkably scanty. It was only in the last 25 years of the nineteenth century that the reptiles were summoned with greater accuracy 'from the abyss of time,' with finds that were measured by the ton and that sparked off some of the most acrimonious scientific disputes ever known.

In Europe the most dramatic find was at Bernissart, Belgium, near the French border. Here in 1878 coal miners encountered numerous fossils in a tunnel at a depth of more than 1000 feet. A paleontologist from the Belgian Natural History Museum identified the bones as those of iguanodons, which were apparently present in enormous numbers. Museum staff then spent three arduous years digging out the skeletons. The mine was a veritable *Iguanodon* graveyard. Uncounted numbers of skeletons were piled vertically through the layered shales and coals in an underground pit that had once been a ravine. The men worked under great difficulty – doubled up, breathing bad air and with poor illumination – yet they managed to map their progress in intricate detail, noting the positions of the brittle bones and transporting them meticulously to the museum. The first skeleton was

Some of the Bernissart iguanodons researched by Dollo rear up in Brussels' Royal Museum.

Dollo's workmen reconstruct an *Iguanodon* in 1880 in a chapel being used temporarily as a museum workshop.

Terrorized by megalosaurs, a herd of iguanodons have fled down a steep ravine into marshy ground. Now threatened by rising waters, most are trapped

in mud. The young can swim or climb to safety, but the adults will perish – to be found millennia later, in 1878, deep under Bernissart, Belgium.

mounted in 1883. Today there are 11 complete standing skeletons with a score of other partially completed ones on show as they were found. It is a unique assembly of a single dinosaur species.

The iguanodons of Bernissart became the life work of one scientist, Louis Dollo, a solemn looking man with heavy, drooping moustaches. For 20 years he labored to understand how the iguanodons – and the other fossils found in the mine – had lived and died. Dollo, who successively ran the museum and then the paleontology department at the University of Brussels, was a prodigious worker. In just one year, 1887, he published the incredible total of 94 scientific papers. He became in effect the world's only iguanodontologist, yet he never wrote a definitive work on the *Iguanodon*. Instead he published his findings in masses of individual papers, often in a clipped telegraphic style. He once said of a certain project: 'I am not close to the end of my work; it is not as yet sufficiently brief.'

Dollo concluded that he was dealing with two different species of *Iguanodon* but the differences between them are so small that other workers believe they may be accounted for by the differences between the sexes. His work confirmed something that others had strongly suspected – that iguanodons were not the four-footed creatures portrayed by Owen and Hawkins but were bipedal. He also showed that the odd horn-like structure which Hawkins had placed on *Iguanodon's* nose was in fact its thumb, a spike to be used for defense. He also revealed that the tail was strengthened by interlinking complexes of tendons which acted like cables. The tail could apparently be held straight out behind the creature as a balancing device when it ran and perhaps also used as a club in self-defense.

Dollo was able to paint quite an accurate picture of how the iguanodons lived and died. They occupied a section of coast to the south-east of the delta area in which the Oxford fossils had been found. In this lush, tropical environment, the iguanodons, ready to flee at the approach of predatory megalosaurs, browsed on the ferns which also provided cover for crocodiles, turtles and frogs in the ponds and rivers of the coastal area.

Dollo noted that in his ravine there were no young animals, and guessed 'that the iguanodons of Bernissart were perhaps the old individuals that had withdrawn to this place to die' (a reference to the myth of an elephants' graveyard, then a popular notion in Europe). In fact it seems more likely that a whole herd of the animals were either driven into the ravine by megalosaurs or were hemmed in while feeding and were unable to escape. No one has yet shown why there were no young iguanodons. It is possible that the ravine was a mud-trap and that the younger, lighter iguanodons were able to escape, leaving the older and heavier creatures to perish in rising flood waters.

Iguanodon, however, represents just one of the many scores of species that were to be known by the end of the nineteenth century. The real spadework – literally and metaphorically – was done in the United States. There, as in England, dinosaur remains of a rather different sort had been known, though not recognized, since the early 1800s.

In 1800 a farm boy named Pliny Moody of South Hadley, Massachusetts, achieved scientific immortality – he is named in all the histories of the subject – by discovering some enormous three-toed footprints imprinted in sandstone. Locals termed them the marks of 'Noah's Raven.' In 1835 the President of Amherst College in Massachusetts, Edward Hitchcock – who was also the Professor of Natural Theology and Geology of the College – began collecting slabs of rock containing fossil footprints. He went on collecting the footprints for the next 30 years. He took the tracks to be those of massive, long-extinct birds. 'I have gone back into those immensely remote ages,' he wrote in 1848, after 13 years of study, 'and watched those shores along which these enormous and heteroclitic beings walked. Now I have seen, in scientific vision, an apterous [i.e. wingless] bird some 12 or 15 feet high, – nay, large flocks of them – walking over the muddy surface, followed by many others of analogous character but of smaller size'. Ten years later he published his massive work, the *Ichnology of New England*, which identifies 50 different types of track. But he never did connect the footprints with dinosaurs. In 1861 Hitchcock learnt of the discovery in the quarries of Solnhofen, Germany of the first bird, *Archaeopteryx*, which neatly combines the features of both bird and reptile. He died three years later, believing his views vindicated. By that time they seemed eccentric; now – given the debate over the actual relationship between birds and dinosaurs – they seem quite far-sighted.

The man who actually introduced the New World to its own dinosaurs was Joseph Leidy. Leidy, a gentle and dignified man, developed a passion for natural history as a schoolboy and often played truant from school to wander through the fields and woods outside his native Philadelphia. He trained as a doctor but found he had little aptitude for practical medicine and developed instead his talent for the study of the anatomy of vertebrates. In 1852 he planned to go with a friend of his to collect fossils in the far West. He did not go. The anatomy professor at the University of Pennsylvania died and Leidy was offered the appointment. He never did go into the field: the countless fossils he studied and described were all sent to him. It seemed to make no difference to his work: he became a solid professional and his width of knowledge, his expertise, and his careful thinking gave him an international reputation.

In 1855 an official expedition party surveying the Judith River, in what was then Nebraska Territory (now Montana), found some large fossil teeth in one of the Judith's windblasted outcrops. The teeth were sent to Leidy, who announced with delight the discovery of the first American dinosaurs. They were of two species which seemed ideal counterparts to England's plant-eating *Iguanodon* and predatory *Megalosaurus*. The plant-eater he named *Trachodon* ('rugged tooth'). Its supposed predator he called *Deinodon horridus* ('the horrible terror tooth'). He eagerly awaited the find of a complete dinosaur skeleton.

When it appeared, three years later, it was something of a surprise, for the creature, clearly a herbivore, was nothing like the Crystal Palace reconstructions. In 1858 William Foulke, a fellow scientist from Philadelphia, was staying at Haddonfield, New Jersey, just across the Delaware River. There he learned that fossil bones had been found some 20 years previously in an old marl (or clayey limestone) pit. The pit had largely been filled in but workmen indicated the position of the finds and Foulke began excavations. Ten feet down, he unearthed some large, brittle bones that were handed over to Leidy. In December 1858 Leidy published his description. They were, he said, the bones of a close relative of *Iguanodon*, which he named *Hadrosaurus foulkii* (this find has since given its name to a whole group of related dinosaurs – the hadrosaurs – all duck-billed).

Leidy had enough to build up a detailed picture of the *Hadrosaurus* – teeth, a fragment of jaw, 28 vertebrae, fore and hind limbs, the hind feet, and parts of the pelvis. To his amazement there was a considerable disparity in size between the four-foot front limbs and the six-foot hind legs. The creature would have made a most ungainly quadruped, and it entirely contradicted

What Color were Dinosaurs?

To this question – one constantly asked of paleontologists by members of the public – there is no ready answer. Color cannot be preserved in the fossil record. Even when the skin itself is fossilized, giving a good idea of texture, it is impossible to know what its color was in life.

But it is possible to make an informed – if generalized – guess at an answer. Color is vital to survival in countless species. It acts as camouflage, as a warning, as sexual attractant, as a device to mimic other creatures. Small animals like insects, which must survive the predatory attentions of numerous other creatures, show the greatest range of color adaptations. Mammals, to which dinosaurs may be compared in their life-styles, show a less dramatic range. Their coloration is defined largely by the need to hide from predators or avoid being seen by would-be prey.

The world of the dinosaurs was not so different in its colors from tropical regions today, and the dinosaurs' adaptations to their environments would – as far as color is concerned – be comparable to those displayed by today's large tropical mammals. Dinosaurs had to blend with the leafy shadows of woodlands, the greens and browns of marshy areas, the yellows and duns of open savannah (though the actual color may not have been as important as the tone: dinosaurs, like modern lizards and most mammals, were probably color-blind).

Iguanodons, which needed copious supplies of plants and had little defense against a predator other than their bulk, could thus have been greeny-brown. Sauropods may have been crocodile colored to match them with waterside habitats. Some dinosaurs may even have been striped, as zebras and tigers are, to baffle the eye in open grassland.

Joseph Leidy, who identified the first dinosaurs found in the New World, was a dignified, modest and gentle man, as well as one of the greatest anatomists of his day.

Hadrosaurus foulkii – named after William Foulke, who first identified the site where the bones were found – stands in a Princeton museum in 1878, correctly restored in its upright stance.

the reconstruction with which the world was now familiar through the work of Owen and Hawkins. Leidy guessed that 'this great extinct herbivorous lizard may have been in the habit of browsing, sustaining itself, kangaroo-like, in an erect position on its back extremities and tail.' He was right, and America had acquired the world's first dinosaur correctly reconstructed.

It was not until the 1870s however, that the New World began to reveal the true wealth of its dinosaur remains. In the words of Adrian Desmond, in his book *The Hot-Blooded Dinosaurs*, 'the monsters sprang fully formed from the earth.' That they did so was largely due to one of the most virulent scientific disputes of the century, between two arch rivals, Othniel Marsh of Yale and Edward Cope of Philadelphia.

Marsh was the son of a New England farmer. He might have remained in obscurity but for an inheritance that he received when he was 21 from his uncle, George Peabody. Peabody was a man of fabulous wealth, a partner of the banker Julius Morgan. He was also a man who felt his own lack of education and was keen to find worthy uses for his money – he built institutes and museums (both Harvard and Yale have museums named after him), he endowed academic chairs, he provided scholarships.

Marsh began a long-term scheme that would both benefit himself and put Uncle George's money to good use. First he gave himself a belated education; then, in 1856, he received Uncle George's backing to enter Yale, where, because of his age, he was variously known as 'Daddy' or 'Captain.' After six years at Yale and some study abroad in Europe, Marsh, who now had secure academic credentials, persuaded Peabody to endow Yale with a new museum at which Marsh was to be Professor of Paleontology. The university was delighted with the gift and happy to appoint Marsh a professor. He now devoted himself full time to fossils and in the years that followed he became one of the world's most eminent paleontologists. He was for twelve years the President of the National Academy of Sciences. But he was a dry, prickly and self-centred character. He never married, and lived alone in an 18-room brownstone house in New Haven, free to organize as he saw best the financial and scientific resources at his command.

Edward Drinker Cope had very different beginnings. His father was a devout and wealthy Quaker shipowner. His mother died when he was three. Cope was a precocious child. At six, he was already taking notes on the skeleton of an ichthyosaur in Philadelphia. From his teens, he was driven by some fairly unprepossessing characteristics – ambition, jealousy, pride – into a brilliant career in science. At 18 he published his first scientific paper (on salamanders). He wrote 30 scientific papers *before* beginning his formal zoological education at the University of Pennsylvania. At 24 he became Professor of Zoology at Haverford College, and thereafter he devoted his life to the study of natural history, in which he was a master of three fields: modern fishes, modern amphibians and reptiles, and fossil vertebrates. His output was extraordinary – his published works number nearly 1400. In his style, he was the opposite to Marsh. He flitted from subject to subject as whim seized him. He lived simply – he had to, for some bad investments dissipated the family fortune – and he worked with little professional assistance. He was too much of an individualist to be much of an organization man and in 1866 he resigned his academic post to devote himself full time to fossils at Haddonfield, where the hadrosaur had been discovered.

His move at once proved lucky. He found the skeleton of Leidy's *Deinodon* and revealed it to be even more kangaroo-like than *Hadrosaurus*. It was, he suggested, a leaping predator that could disembowel its prey with its hind feet. He called it *Laelaps* (Hurricane) — the name of a dog in Greek mythology which was turned to stone in a leaping pose.

The differences between the two men were bound to lead to acrimony. Both had chosen the same field of study but in all other ways they differed. Marsh – dry, pedantic, rich, over 30 before he published anything, backed by all the resources of the academic community; and Cope – young, aggressive, poor, feverishly brilliant (yet also more prone to error). What might they have achieved had they worked together? Perhaps a lot less – their rivalry inspired both of them, and the result was a revolution in scientific and popular knowledge of the age of reptiles.

Their differences developed into open rivalry in 1870. Cope had recovered a skeleton of a plesiosaur, unlike any yet known. It was a 50-foot creature with a 25-foot neck. He had named it *Elasmosaurus* ('ribbon reptile') and set it up in the Philadelphia Museum. Marsh – at this time a professional colleague – came to see it and pointed out that Cope had misunderstood the find – all the vertebrae were the wrong way round. Cope was incensed and angrily rejected the suggestion. He rapidly found out that Marsh was correct and in his embarrassment tried to buy up all the copies of his original description.

For a few years, the two men steered clear of each other. Cope went off to the Judith River in Montana with another great dinosaur hunter, Charles Sternberg, and unearthed a horned dinosaur, *Monoclonius*.

Then in 1877, a schoolmaster and an Oxford graduate, Arthur Lakes, who had emigrated to the West, discovered some huge bones in a line of Rocky Mountain foothills, near Morrison, Colorado. He sent some of the fossils to both Marsh and Cope. Meanwhile a friend of Lakes', O W Lucas, found equally gigantic bones near Canyon City, Colorado. These bones Lucas sent to Cope – and the race was on.

Marsh sent off one of his own collectors in Kansas, Benjamin Mudge, to find Lakes. Soon Mudge cabled 'satisfactory arrangement made for two months. Jones (i.e. Cope) cannot interfere.' Within a few weeks Lakes and Mudge had shipped a ton of bones by rail to Marsh, among which were the first remains of a plated dinosaur, *Stegosaurus*, and of a massive herbivore (one thigh-bone was eight feet long), which Marsh described in June 1877 and named *Titanosaurus*. He also added that Cope's *Laelaps* was a false name: it had already been given to other creatures. Marsh renamed Cope's find *Dryptosaurus*.

Cope meanwhile was relying on Lucas for his bones, some of which were those of another giant herbivore. In August 1877 Cope described and named his find – *Camarasaurus* ('chambered reptile,' named after the hollowed out, open structure of its vertebrae). In retaliation for Marsh's dig on the name of *Laelaps*, Cope snidely claimed that *he* was the first to describe a giant herbivore, because Marsh's choice of *Titanosaurus* as a name had just been given a few months previously to a similar fossil found by an English paleontologist, Richard Lydekker. Marsh had to change the name of his find to *Atlantosaurus*.

The same year, Marsh received a letter signed 'Harlow & Edwards' giving news of a huge collection of fossil bones at Como Bluff, Wyoming (near Medicine Bow, known to all addicts of the TV series *The Virginian*). Mudge accompanied by a new collector, Samuel Williston, set out for the quarry (Williston let it be known that he was going to Oregon, just in case Cope's men heard they were off). The two contacted 'Harlow & Edwards,' and found them to be two Union Pacific Railroad workers, William Carlin and

Othniel Marsh, of Yale, established an immense reputation for scholarship and a correspondingly immense collection of fossils – facts recalled by the cartoon in which Marsh 'shows his perfect mastery over the *Ceratopsidae*.'

William Reed. The site – an east-west ridge that paralleled the railroad – was truly extraordinary. Williston reported that the bones 'extended for *seven* miles and are by the ton.' Marsh determined to keep the site to himself but within a few days one of Cope's men appeared. 'He first purported to be selling groceries!!' reported Williston, who managed to obtain a sample of the man's handwriting to check that it was not Cope himself who was prying.

Como Bluff was worked continuously by Marsh's men from 1877 to 1883. Conditions were harsh. Lakes, who joined the team, recorded hailstorms, sandstorms, snowdrifts, temperatures of − 58°C, and on one occasion a plague of lizards. But the dig was a triumph. It uncovered many tons of dinosaur bones in over a hundred quarries. Of the many scores of species unearthed for Marsh, perhaps the most dramatic were those of the giant, four-footed plant-eaters whose bones emerged in such profusion that Marsh made a special study of them. He named them 'sauropods' or 'lizard feet' on account of their five toes (as opposed to the three toes of the bipeds).

Cope had meanwhile been digging at Cañon City, with occasional forays into enemy territory. Several times his men were warned off with threats. Some workers deserted to the opposite camp. Marsh opened and closed quarries at breakneck speed, stripping each new one of its fossils in a matter of a few weeks. Once Bill Reed even smashed some remaining fossils so that Cope should not have any duplicates in case he should happen along. Another time Cope even arrived himself, to the great surprise of Arthur Lakes. To Lakes' even greater surprise, he rather took to Cope. He reported to Marsh: 'the *monstrum horrendum* has been and gone and I must say that what I saw of him I liked very much.'

Of the giant sauropods, the most impressive by far was that of the *Brontosaurus*, the favorite of countless museum exhibits and picture books. *Brontosaurus*, which reached over 70 feet in length, means 'thunder lizard.' Marsh noted with amazement the tiny head, which was only a few inches across and smaller than some of the neck vertebrae that supported it. Its estimated weight – 30 or 40 tons – and its tiny brain, which weighed only a few ounces, forcibly suggested to Marsh a portrait that has remained popular to the present day. 'The very small head and brain and slender neural cord indicate a stupid, slow moving reptile … *Brontosaurus* was more or less amphibious and its food was probably aquatic plants or succulent vegetation.' Marsh placed the large sauropods in water because he could not imagine their bulk being moved successfully on land for a long period. But in describing it as a slow moving, cumbersome stupid animal that liked to support itself in water, Marsh made another contribution to the lasting controversy about dinosaur physiology.

The end of this great period of dinosaur hunting was symbolized by the row that surrounded the skeleton of *Diplodocus*, the longest – though not the heaviest – of the lot. Marsh found some bits of *Diplodocus* but he never found a complete skeleton. It was the hope of all hunters to do so. The great find was finally achieved at the turn of the century, thanks to the determination and cash of Andrew Carnegie, self-made man, millionaire and philanthropist. Carnegie not only accumulated tremendous amounts of wealth, he also redistributed it on a grand scale. One of his foundations was the Carnegie Institute in his home town of Pittsburgh. Between 1895 and 1905 he poured into his brain-child 25 million dollars, part of which financed several fossil collecting parties.

In 1899 and 1900 one of these parties unearthed the first complete skeleton of a *Diplodocus*, in Albany County, Wyoming. When reconstructed, *Diplodocus*

Edward Drinker Cope, Marsh's great rival, was an acknowledged genius. He made his first scientific observations at the age of six, published his first scientific paper at 18 and completed some 1400 works in his life.

carnegiei, as it was suitably entitled, turned out to be just over 87 feet long, by far the longest land animal ever known. The fame of the model spread rapidly. Carnegie kindly had the entire model duplicated several times and plaster casts were sent to Germany, France, Austria, Italy, Argentina, Mexico and England, at a cost of about $30,000 each. In each place the skeleton was remounted according to the original reconstruction as a sort of reptilian version of an elephant, rising high up on massive vertical legs.

This reconstruction pointed to a contradiction in the way in which dinosaurs were regarded. If they were gigantic lizards, would the *Diplodocus* really have stood in that position? Should it not be portrayed with its limbs splayed out, crocodile fashion, to either side? Some argued that it was so massive that it could never have raised itself and must have had splayed limbs so that it could take frequent rests by lowering itself to the ground. Others

BROWN EXCAVATING A DUCK-BILLED DINOSAUR.

LOADING UP.

These pictures, taken on a 1912 expedition headed by one of the greatest dinosaur collectors, Barnum Brown, give an idea of the physical difficulties faced by fossil prospectors around the turn of the century. To identify fossil-bearing beds in the unmapped immensities of the mid-West, to hack out the bones and to transport them, imposed on fossil hunters a life as harsh as any faced by the pioneers.

HAULING FOSSILS OUT OF THE RED DEER VALLEY.

The brontosaur, unearthed between 1909 and 1922 thanks to backing from Andrew Carnegie, was given the scientific name of *Apatosaurus louisiae*, after Carnegie's wife, Louise. This shot, taken during reconstruction work, shows the hips (left), the thorax and part of the neck.

argued exactly the opposite – that such a bulk could not have been carried on anything but straight legs.

Every specialist in America and Europe had a say in the debate. A German paleontologist, Gustav Tornier, drew the creature with splayed limbs, a tail dragging on the ground and its neck bent into an S shape. The Director of the Carnegie Museum, W J Holland, sneered at Tornier's reconstruction, as 'a skeletal monstrosity.' If it walked with splayed limbs, Holland said, its rib cage would have been several feet below the surface on which it walked; Tornier's *Diplodocus* would have needed to walk along above a deep trench! (Holland's view was vindicated in 1938 when at Glen Rose, Texas, the track of a 60-foot *Brontosaurus* was found. The monster had 12-foot strides and yet the trail was only six feet wide. Had it walked like a crocodile with its legs splayed sideways, the trail would have been a good 20 feet wide.)

Between them, Marsh, Cope and the other researchers had given the earth a new past. Before Marsh and Cope, there were just nine species of dinosaur known, linked by Owen's concept of a great race of reptiles, the Dinosauria. Marsh and Cope *alone* discovered 136 new species of dinosaur and built collections that are housed respectively in the Peabody Museum, Yale and the American Museum of Natural History in New York. By the 1890s they had also established the science of dinosaur hunting in its present form. They had shown the advantage of getting out into the field rather than relying on chance finds. They had devised methods for recording, removing and preserving fossil finds (by coating them in plaster of Paris and splints). They and others in Europe and America had revealed the full range of the creatures – the carnivorous bipeds, the giant four-footed plant-eaters, the bipedal herbivores, and the plated, armored and horned quadrupeds – all in addition to the other reptilian forms that inhabited the water and air.

But how were they all to be classified? How did they evolve? How did they live? How did they die out? How were they related? *When* exactly did they live? The problems were immense – but at least by the end of the nineteenth century there was sufficient information to pose such problems – and hope for realistic answers.

Dinosaur Hunting in the Old West

Charles Hazelius Sternberg was one of the most successful fossil hunters ever. Born in 1850, he grew to manhood just in time to take part in the golden age of fossil hunting in the American West, 1870–1910. When much of the country west of the Mississippi was still uncharted wilderness, Sternberg became the first to explore many famous collecting localities, enduring numerous hardships and making great discoveries. He was active for 60 of the 93 years that he lived, and his many hundreds of fossil finds enriched museum collections in both North America and Europe. Although he possessed no degrees he became one of the most respected authorities on fossil restoration in the world, serving for a time as Head Collector and Preparator of Vertebrate Fossils for the Geological Survey of Canada. In recognition of his contributions to science, at least 18 species were named in his honor.

Sternberg was also an accomplished writer of prose and poetry. His autobiography, 'Life of a Fossil Hunter', recalls as no other work has ever done the rigors and excitement of the early days of dinosaur hunting. In this extract he recalls his adventures at the age of 25, as he is about to begin his first expedition to the Kansas chalk with Edward Cope, whose extraordinary toughness of character emerges powerfully from Sternberg's description:

'What vivid memories I have of that first expedition! – memories of countless hardships and splendid results. I explored all the exposures of chalk from the mouth of Hackberry Creek, in the eastern part of Gove County, to Fort Wallace, on the south fork of the Smoky Hill, a distance of a hundred miles, as well as the region along the north and south forks of the Soloman River.

When we left Buffalo Station, we left civilization behind us. We made our own wagon trails, two of which especially were afterwards used by the settlers until the section lines were constructed . . .

There was constant danger from Indians, and in order that we might escape as much as possible the eagle eye of some scout who might be passing through the country, our tent and wagon-sheet were of brown duck. This blended with the dry, brown buffalo grass, as we traveled from canyon to canyon and could not be distinguished very far even by the trained eye of an Indian.

I never carried my rifle with me. I left it in camp or in the wagon, for I soon decided that I could not hunt Indians and fossils at the same time, and I was there for fossils . . .

Perhaps a description of a typical day's experience in one of the long ravines that gash the southern slope of the country may be of interest to my readers . . .

My first step must be to find water and pitch a camp. But often I have no idea where water is to be found, and must give as much care to the search as if I were looking for fossils. So while the driver follows me with the wagon, I hunt for water and fossils at the same time.

Both sides of my ravine are bordered with cream-colored, or yellow, chalk, with blue below. Sometimes for hundreds of feet the rock is entirely denuded and cut into lateral

STERNBERG.

ravines, ridges, and mounds, or beautifully sculptured into tower and obelisk. Sometimes it takes on the semblance of a ruined city, with walls of tottering masonry, and only a near approach can convince the eye that this is only another example of that mimicry in which nature so frequently indulges. The chalk beds are entirely bare of vegetation, with the exception of a desert shrub that "finds a foothold in the rifted rock" and sends its roots down every crevice. This shrub is one of the fossil hunter's worst enemies. Sending its roots down the clefts in the rock, it searches out the fossil bones that have been preserved there, and feasts upon them until they have been entirely consumed, thus thriving at the expense of God's buried dead . . .

All this time I am wandering along the canyon in search of water . . . I know that there is water at the river but it is so far away from my work that I go on and on in the hope of finding some nearer at hand. Dinnertime comes, and the day is so hot that perspiration flows from every pore. A howling south wind rises and fills our eyes with clouds of pure lime dust, inflaming them almost beyond human endurance. Still no water. The driver, with horses famishing for it, makes frantic gestures to me to hurry. To ease my parched lips and swelling tongue, I roll a pebble around in my mouth or, if the season is propitious, allay my thirst with the acid juice of a red berry that grows in the ravines.

After hours of search, I find in moist ground the borings of crawfishes; with line and sinker I measure the depth to water a couple of feet below in these miniature wells. The welcome signal is given to Will, the driver, and he digs a well, so that both man and beast may be supplied.

If I could sum up all the sufferings, I endured in the chalk fossil fields, I should say that I suffered more from the lack of good drinking water than from all the other ills combined. Except when we were in the vicinity of one of the half-dozen springs that are scattered about over an expanse of country 100 miles long and 40 wide, the only water that we had to drink was alkali water, which has the same effect upon the body as a solution of Epsom salts, constantly weakening the system. Yet whole neighborhoods of settlers to this day have no other water for themselves or their beasts, and they show the deteriorating effects in their faces and their walk. If I have found, scattered along a wash, the bones of some fossil fish or reptile, as soon as we have pitched camp and eaten our meal of antelope meat, hot biscuits and coffee, we both return with pick and shovel, and, carefully saving each weathered fragment, trace the remains to where the rest of the bones lie *in situ*, as the scientists say, that is, in their original position in their rocky sepulcher.

Then comes the work in the hot sun, whose rays are reflected with added fervor from the glaring surface of the chalk. Every blow of the pick loosens a cloud of chalk dust, which is carried by the wind into our eyes. But we labor on with unfailing enthusiasm until we have laid bare a floor space upon which I can stretch myself out at full length. Lying there on the blistering chalk in the burning sun, and working carefully and patiently with brush and awl, I uncover enough of the bones so that I can tell what I have found, and so that when I cut out the rock which holds them I shall not cut into the bones themselves.

After they have been traced, if they lie in good, hard rock, a ditch is cut around them, and by repeated blows of the pick, the slab which contains them is loosened.

This is then securely wrapped and strengthened with plaster, or with burlap bandages that have been dipped in plaster of the consistency of cream. In the case of large specimens, boards are put lengthwise to assist in strengthening the material, so that it will bear transportation. Later I hope to tell of a method originated by me, by which the most delicate fossil, even if preserved in very loose, friable rock, may be detached and transported safely . . .

All day, from the first streak of light until the last level ray forced me to leave the work, I toiled on, forgetting the heat and the miserable thirst and the alkali water, forgetting everything but the one great object of my life – to secure from the crumbling strata of this old ocean bed the fossil remains of the fauna of Cretaceous Times.

The incessant labor, however, had a weakening effect upon my system so that I fell a victim to malaria, and when a violent attack of shaking ague came on, I felt as if fate were indeed against me.

I remember how, one day, when I was in the midst of a shaking fit, I found a beautiful specimen of a Kansas mosasaur. *Clidastes tortor* Cope named it, because an additional set of articulations in the backbone enabled it to coil. Its head lay in the center, with the column around it, and the four paddles stretched out on either side. It was covered by only a few inches of distintegrated chalk.

Forgetting my sickness, I shouted to the surrounding wilderness "Thank God! Thank God!" And I did well to thank the Creator, as I slowly brushed away the powdered chalk and revealed the beauties of this reptile of the Age of Reptiles.

"How fleet is a glance of the mind!" Instead of an arid, treeless plain, covered with short grass, a great semi-tropical ocean lies at our feet. Everywhere along the shores and estuaries are great forests of magnolia, birch, sassafras, and fig, while a vast expanse of blue water stretches southward.

"But," you ask, "what is that animal at full length upon the water in that sheltered cove?"

Watch it a moment! It raises a long conical head, four feet in length and set firmly upon a neck of seven strongly spined vertebrae. This powerful head terminates in a long, bony rostrum, also conical in shape . . .

But see! an enemy in the distance is attracting our reptile's attention. It sets its four powerful paddles in motion, and unrolling its forked tongue from beneath its windpipe, throws it forward with a threatening hiss, the only note of defiance it can raise. The flexible body and long eel-like tail set up their serpentine motion, and the vast mass of animal life, over 30 feet in length, rushes forward with ever-increasing speed through water that foams away on either side and gurgles in a long wake behind.

The great creature strikes its opponent with the impact of a racing yacht and piercing heart and lungs with its powerful ram, leaves a bleeding wreck upon the water. Then raising its head and fore paddles into the air, it bids defiance to the whole brute creation, of which it is monarch. . . .

Watch that ripple! It is caused by a shoal of mackerel scurrying in toward shallow water, in a mighty column five feet deep. They are flying for their lives, for they have seen behind them their most terrible enemy, a monster fish with a muzzle like a bulldog's and huge fangs three inches long projecting from its mouth. Two rows of horrid teeth, one above and one below, complete its armature. The great jaws, 14 inches long and four deep, move on a fulcrum, and when they have dropped to seize a multitude of these little fish, they close with a vice-like power. The crushed and mangled remains pass down a cavernous throat to appease a voracious appetite.

The powerful front fins are armed with an outer ray that moves on a joint in the pectoral arch, a long recurved piece of solid bone, enameled on the outer side and more powerful as a weapon than a cavalryman's sword. This single-edge sword is three feet long, and commands the respect of its owner's enemies, the great saurians, or Kansas mosasaurs. Our fish has only to swim up close to the abdomen of a sleeping reptile, and lay it open for several feet with one sudden stroke. If that is not sufficient, a slap of the powerful tail, with a span of nearly four feet, finishes the work.

But see! nearer and nearer the great fish comes, mouthful and mouthful of the fishes falling into its horrid jaws. It must be starving; so eager is it for its prey that it seems unconscious of the fact that the tide has turned and is moving outward. Now it discovers its danger and turns but too late. The water has gone back to the deep, leaving it struggling for breath in a shallow pool. It thrashes wildly about with its tail, whose sticky secretions help to envelop it more and more thickly with mud and slime, until at last its struggles cease.

And then the scene changes. The old ocean disappears and we stand, George and I, 3000 feet above sea level, on Hay Creek, in Logan County, among crumbling ruins of denuded and eroded chalk; and working with pick and shovel in the burning sun, we bring the mighty carcass once more to the light of day.

I will pass on now to my expedition in the Bad Lands with Professor Cope. . . . About the first of August 1876 Mr Isaac and I were in Omaha, awaiting the arrival of Professor Cope from Philadelphia.

We met him at the depot, and I remember his watching me with astonishment as I limped along the street on my crippled leg. At last turning to Isaac, whom he knew to be a horseman, he asked, "Can Mr Sternberg ride a horse?"

Isaac answered: "I've seen him mount a pony bareback and cut out one of his mares from a herd of wild horses."

That satisfied the Professor, and when we got to Montana, he gave me the worst-tempered pony in the bunch.

We were soon hurrying along over the treeless plains of Nebraska, gaining in altitude every hour, until we reached the highlands of the Great Divide and plunged down into Weber and Echo canyons, whose forests are dwarfed into miniatures by the majesty of the mountains about them.

It was the first time that I had ever been among these stupendous cliffs and ranges

FOSSIL-HUNTING ON THE RED DEER RIVER.

and I held my breath for very wonder as they unfolded before my astonished vision. They soon became familiar sights enough, but never, even when I gazed every day upon the three Tetons, with the snow glistening in their gorges in midsummer, or upon the mighty ranges of the Rockies, did I lose my feeling of awe at the power here displayed by the almighty Architect who carved these wonderful canyons and set these towering peaks as solemn sentinels over the works of His hands.

We had the pleasure of Mrs Cope's company as far as Ogden. Then we three men, taking the narrow-gauge railway, went on to Franklin, Idaho. Here the most uncomfortable journey I have ever experienced awaited us – 600 miles in a Concord coach, through the dry, barren plains of Idaho. Our six horses raised clouds of fine dust, which penetrated our clothing and filled our eyes and ears, and, sticking to the perspiration that oozed from every pore, soon gave us the appearance of having the jaundice.

I cannot begin to describe the discomforts of that terrible ride. We traveled ten miles an hour, day and night, stopping only for meals, which cost us a dollar each, and consisted of hot soda biscuit, black coffee, bacon, and mustard, without butter, milk, or eggs. If, worn out from continued loss of sleep, we dozed off for a moment, a sudden lurch of the coach into a chuck-hole would break our heads against a post or a neighbor's head. I remember that once when the Professor was almost exhausted from lack of sleep I took his head in my arms

and held it there, so that he might get a few hours' rest. . . .

When we reached the mountains, the beauty of the scenery and the absence of dust made the journey more endurable but we had to walk up all the steep ascents.

At Helena we laid off for a few days. There the news was fresh from the battlefield, of Custer and the brave men who had followed him to death. A letter of his, written just before he entered the valley of death, was read to us by the proprietor of the hotel. I remember one sentence of it: "We have found the Indians, and are going in after them. We may not come out alive."

All was excitement, and the Professor was strongly advised against the folly of going into the neutral ground between the Sioux and their hereditary enemies, the Crows. A member of either tribe might kill us, and lay our death to the other tribe.

Cope, however, reasoned that now was our time to go into this region, since every able-bodied Sioux would be with the braves under Sitting Bull, while the squaws and children would be hidden away in some fastness of the mountains. There would be no danger for us, he argued, until the Sioux were driven north by the soldiers who were gathering under Terry and Crook for the final struggle.

Judging from past experience, he concluded that we should have nearly three months in which to make our collections in peace. We would leave the field, he said, when we learned that the great chief was being so closely pressed as to be forced to seek safety in flight to the soil of Great Britain, across the Sweet Grass Mountains into Assiniboia.

His judgment proved good. It was not until November, when a heavy snowstorm had covered both the fossil fields and grass for the ponies, that Sitting Bull gave up the unequal struggle against cold and the Boys in Blue, and retreated to a more friendly soil.

At Fort Benton we found a typical frontier town of that day – streets paved with playing-cards, and whisky for sale in open saloons and groceries. Our presence had been heralded abroad during our stay in Helena and the Professor had difficulty in securing an outfit without paying an exorbitant price for it. . . .

All about us stretched the interminable labyrinths of the Bad Lands. Above us lay 1200 feet of denuded rock, which Cope at that time believed to belong to several formations. The rock consists of great beds of black shale, which disintegrates on the sur-

face into a fine, black dust. The lower levels contain many beds of lignite, which makes a good soft coal, and burns readily. We found beds four feet thick along the canyons. All one had to do was to drive up to the face of the cliff and load a wagon in a few minutes.

As soon as the first streak of daylight appeared, we breakfasted and were off, our picks tied to our saddles, our collecting-bags dangling from the pommels, and a lunch of cold bacon and hardtack in our saddle-bags.

I usually rode beside the Professor, my mount a treacherous black mustang, who was ever on the watch to regain his liberty. A curb bit that almost tore his mouth to pieces was my only means of restraining him. My right ear being totally deaf, I usually rode at the Professor's right, when the trail would admit of our traveling abreast. He was not always in a talkative mood but when he began to speak of the wonderful animals of this earth, those of long ago and those of today, so absorbed did he become in his subject that he talked on as if to himself, looking straight ahead and rarely turning toward me, while I listened entranced.

On the very top of the Bad Lands were the Judith River beds . . . Here tablelands and level prairies offered plenty of grass for our ponies; so we climbed to these heights, picketed our horses, and went into the gorges in search of fossils. It was necessary to give the loose shale the most careful examination, as only a streak of dust a little different in color from the uniform black around it, indicated where the bones were buried.

As a result of the loose composition of this friable black shale and the overlying rocks of sandstone, the Missouri has lowered its bed 1200 feet below the level of the prairies, and the whole country is cut up by a perfect labyrinth of canyons and lateral ravines into a dreary landscape of utter barrenness.

At night the view from above of these intricate passages was appalling. The black material of which the rocks are composed did not permit a single ray of light to penetrate the depths below, and the ebony-like darkness seemed dense enough to cut.

Long ridges, terminating in perpendicular cliffs, whose bases impinge upon the river a thousand feet below, extend back into the country for miles. Often they are cut by lateral ravines into peaks and pinnacles, obelisks and towers, and other fantastic forms. These ridges are so narrow that we could hardly walk along them, and their sides drop at an angle of 45°. It was only the disintegrated shale on the surface, into which our feet sank at every step, that gave us a foothold and kept us from shooting with frightful velocity into the gorges below.

One day the Professor asked me to climb to a point near the summit of a lofty ridge, crowned by two massive ledges of sandstone, four feet thick, which projected over the steep slope like the window sills of some Titanic building. These ledges, one above the other and separated by 60 feet of shale, had been swept clean for about three feet, so that I found an easy pathway for my feet, when after laborious climbing I reached the lower ledge. From my lofty perch I had a bird's-eye view of mile upon mile of the wonderful Bad Lands, a scene of desolation such as no pen can picture.

It was my duty to search every square inch of the dust-covered slope between the ledges for fossil bones. After much unsuccessful effort, I came to a place at the head of a gorge, where a perpendicular escarpment dropped downward for a thousand feet. The upper ledge of sandstone had broken loose for a space of 30 feet, and this huge mass of rock, four feet thick, carrying with it the loose dirt and polishing the underlying surface as it thundered down the slope, and struck the lower ledge with such force that it too had broken loose and plunged downward into the abyss. A grove of pine trees at the base of the cliff had been crushed to the earth by this avalanche. To my view the remaining trees, which I knew to be about 50 feet high, appeared like seedlings, and the vast mass of rock like a cobblestone.

I concluded that I should have no difficulty in crawling across the smooth space, for I reasoned that if I began to slip, I could drive the sharp end of my pick into the soft rock and thus stop myself. So climbing up the slope through the loose earth to the base of the upper ledge, I started to cross. When I was halfway over I began to slip, and confidently raising my pick, struck the rock with all my might. God grant that I may never again feel such horror as I felt then, when the pick, upon which I had depended for safety, rebounded as if it had been polished steel, as useless in my hands as a bit of straw. I struck frantically again and yet again but all the time I was sliding down with ever-increasing rapidity toward the edge of the abyss, safety on either side and certain and awful death below.

I remember that I gave up all hope of escape, and that after the first shock I felt no fear of death; but the few moments of my slide seemed hours, measured by the rapidity with which my mind worked. Everything, it seemed to me, that I had ever done or thought spread itself out before my mind's eye as vividly as the wonderful panorama of the cliffs and canyons upon which I had been gazing a few moments before. All the scenes of my life, from childhood up, were re-enacted here with the same emotions of pleasure or pain. I saw distinctly the people I had known, many of them long forgotten. My mother seemed to stand out more prominently than anyone else, and I wondered what she would think when she heard that I had been dashed to pieces. I even planned how, when I did not return to camp, Cope would set out to find me, following my footsteps into the loose dirt until he reached the slide, and I wondered how he would ever get down into the canyon, and how much of my body would be left for burial.

To this day I do not know how I escaped. I suddenly found myself lying on the ledge, on the side I had left a moment before. Probably some part of my clothing, covered with dust as it was, had acted as a brake upon the polished surface. I lay for an hour with trembling knees, too weak to make my way back to camp.

The excitement of our work and the danger with it seemed to make us reckless of life, Professor Cope even more so than the rest of us, although he was at that time United States Paleontologist, and worth a million dollars. I remember one night he was following a buffalo trail to the river, when suddenly his horse stopped and refused to go further. Without dismounting to

IN THE BADLANDS OF ALBERTA.

find out the cause, he plunged his spurs into the animal, and it sprang into the air. Mr Isaac, who was behind, followed. The next day they were surprised to find that they had crossed a gorge ten feet wide, and that but for the keen sight and strength of their horses, they would have been dashed to pieces 100 feet below.

Cope's indefatigability, too, was a constant source of wonder to us. We were in excellent training, after our strenuous outdoor life in the Kansas chalk beds, while he had just been working 14 hours a day in his study and the lithographer's shop, completing a large Government monograph, writing his own manuscript and reading his own proof. When we first met him at Omaha, he was so weak that he reeled from side to side as he walked; yet here he climbed the highest cliffs and walked along the most dangerous ledges, working without intermission from daylight until dark.

Every night when we returned to camp, we found that the cook had spent the whole day in cooking. Exhausted and thirsty – we had no water to drink during the day (all the water in the Bad Lands being like a dense solution of Epsom salts) – we sat down to a supper of cakes and pies and other palatable but indigestible food. Then, when we went to bed, the Professor would soon have a severe attack of nightmare. Every animal of which we had found traces during the day played with him at night, tossing him into the air, kicking him, trampling upon him.

When I waked him, he would thank me cordially and lie down to another attack. Sometimes he would lose half the night in this exhausting slumber. But the next morning he would lead the party and be the last to give up at night. I have never known a more wonderful example of the will's power over the body.

His memory and his imagination, too, were extraordinary. He used to talk to me by the hour, arranging the living and dead animals of the earth in systematic order, giving countless scientific names and their definitions. I forgot the names as soon as I heard them but the loving tribute which he paid to the wonders of creation has had a lasting and helpful effect upon me. If I ever had any feelings of disgust or fear toward any of God's creatures, I lost them upon a knowledge of the animals as revealed to me by the master naturalist, who saw beauty even in lizards and snakes. He believed, and taught me to believe, that it is a crime to destroy life wantonly, any life.

We found no complete specimens of any fossil animals during our stay on Dog Creek but near the summit of the Bad Lands, under beds of yellowish sandstone, we came upon localities literally filled with the scattered bones and teeth of dinosaurs, those terrible lizards whose tread once shook the earth. . . . Among the fragments were pieces of the finely-sculptured shells of the sea turtles, *Trionyx* and *Adocus*, and remains of that strange dinosaur *Trachodon*, whose teeth were arranged as in a magazine, one below another, so that when the old teeth wore out, others were ever ready to take their place.

Part of the time our route lay among the foothills of the Judith River Mountains to the south of us; and when we emerged again on to the open plain, we found ourselves in a great amphitheater, 100 miles across. To the west the towering ranges of the Rockies rose in silent grandeur, their sides scarred deeply with canyons, in whose recesses the white snow gleamed and sparkled in the morning light. To the south, east and north, the Judith River Mountains, the Little Rockies, Medicine Bow, Bearpaw, and the Sweet Grass Mountains on the border line of Assiniboia made up the circle. A glorious scene! And there was exhilaration too in the thought that ours was the first wagon to roll through these rich solitudes, given up for ages to the red hunter and his game. These hills were soon to re-echo with the shriek of the locomotive, and this rich soil to nourish a thousand souls but in the days I am recalling, we did not meet a single human being in all the 40 miles of our journey.

That night, after another hard day, we halted at the head of a short and very steep ravine ending in an open valley between two ridges, whose lofty precipices abutted on the Missouri 1200 feet below.

This valley, Cope told us, was to be our camping ground for some time to come, as a steamboat snubbing-post was situated here. When I learned this, I threw out my roll of blankets and started it on its way to camp. It bounded down the ravine, leaping high in the air from boulder to boulder, and never stopped until it was caught in a bunch of the cactus that covered the level plain below.

Everything but the Professor's trunk was unloaded, and the wagon pulled to the head of the gulch, where Isaac took charge of the tongue, and the Professor and I, each tying a picket rope to the hind axle and making a half-hitch to a convenient sapling, let the wagon slowly down the hill. When the rope was paid out, Isaac blocked the wheels with stones, and we advanced for another hitch, continuing in this way until we reached the bottom. The baggage was then packed down and after a space had been cleared of cactus, our tent was pitched. It was not until long after midnight that we sat down to cook our meal and when we rolled into our blankets we slept the sleep of utter exhaustion.

Not only during this trip but all through our stay in the Bad Lands, we were tormented by myriads of black gnats, which got under our hat rims and shirt sleeves, and produced sores that gave rise to pus and thick scabs. They got under the saddles and girths too, irritating the horses almost beyond endurance. We were forced, for lack of something better, to cover our faces and arms with bacon grease and to rub the skins of the horses under the collars and saddles with the same disagreeable substance.

Fossil bones always partake of the characteristics of the rock in which they are entombed, and here they were quite hard when we got in to where the rock was compact. The Professor found here the first specimen ever discovered in America of the wonderful horned dinosaurs; *Monoclonius* he called the first species. I assisted him in digging out his specimen of *M. crassus*, a species distinguished by a small horn over each orbit and a large one on the nasal bones; and I myself discovered two species new to science.

The species I discovered were collected on the north side of the river, three miles below Cow Island, after the Professor had taken the last boat down the river. When we uncovered these bones we found them very brittle, as they had been shattered by the uplift of the strata in which they were buried; and we were obliged to devise some means of holding them in place. The only thing we had in camp that could be made into a paste was rice, which we had brought along for food. We boiled quantities of it until it became thick, then, dipping into it flour bags and pieces of cotton cloth and burlap, we used them to strengthen the bones and hold them together. This was the beginning of a long line of experiments, which culminated in the recently adopted method of taking up large fossils by bandaging them with strips of cloth dipped in plaster of Paris, like the bandages in which a modern surgeon encases a broken limb.

I feel it a great privilege to have been one of the original discoverers of these great horned dinosaurs, whose skeletons are now among the chief glories of our museums.'

With gillfuls of water, the mudskippers of Borneo venture on to land, recalling the evolutionary leap which, between 400 and 200 million years ago,

2/The Coming of the Dinosaurs

This century, the finds described in the last chapter have been vastly extended. At Vernal, Utah, so many dinosaur bones were found that in 1915 the surrounding area was designated the Dinosaur National Monument. (There, bones are no longer removed: when discovered, they are partially revealed, cleaned and left in position for visitors to see.) New finds have turned up regularly – from Tanzania (the home of the largest dinosaur yet found, *Brachiosaurus*), Mongolia (where the eggs of a horned dinosaur appeared in 1922), Canada, South America, South Africa, China, Germany, Brazil, Australia. Early in the century, it became clear that dinosaurs had once inhabited the whole world (including, presumably, Antarctica, where an early reptile has been found; but because the conditions are so tough, no

transformed fish successively into amphibians and reptiles, among them the early dinosaur *Thecodontosaurus.*

dinosaurs' remains have appeared there yet). The total weight of dinosaur fossils now runs into hundreds of tons. Scientists recognize some 600 species.

Where did the dinosaurs come from? How did they live? How were they all related? Where did they go to? These are the questions that scientists have asked for over a century, and are still asking. In general terms they have some answers and most of this book is concerned with explaining them.

But first, briefly and with inevitably contentious generalizations, let us set the dinosaurs in the context of the history of the earth. The earth was formed about 4500 million years ago. The first rocks of which we have records are 3750 million years old. When they were formed there was no life – just the brownish rock, glinting with spots of mineral, torn by volcanoes, rent by earthquakes, and scoured by the teeming rains that formed the primeval seas. Only the earth, the sea and the air moved. Nothing on land could have survived the sun's ultra-violet radiation, which poured through the ammonia and methane of the primitive atmosphere. The surface of the earth, however, possessed the basic constituents of life – carbon, hydrogen, oxygen and nitrogen. Fired, perhaps, by bolts of lightning, these chemicals were recast to form more complex molecules that in turn recombined to make the first self-replicating molecules. These microscopic organisms sustained themselves by fermentation in the chemicals of the primeval ocean, giving off carbon dioxide. This became the base for new forms of life, containing chlorophyll, an ingredient in the chemical process of photosynthesis, which uses carbon dioxide, water and sunlight to make sugar. Thus freed from dependence upon water-borne chemicals, the first plants arose. A by-product of photosynthesis is oxygen, which plants cannot use. For hundreds of millions of years, oxygen seeped into the atmosphere, slowly transforming it. A thousand million years ago – when the earth's history to date had already run three-quarters of its course – there arose microscopic animals that could make use of the oxygen. Over the millennia, these evolved into primeval sponges, jelly fish, worms, corals and shellfish.

The coming of shellfish marks a sort of base line for the measurement of life on earth, for they left the first true fossils (though impressions of more ancient creatures have been found). This period, which lasted some 100 million years, is known as the Cambrian (named after the Roman term for Wales, where rocks from this time were first researched). The Cambrian is the first period in the second of the four great eras into which the history of the earth is customarily divided. These are the Pre-Cambrian, the Paleozoic ('ancient life'), Mesozoic ('middle life') – the Age of the Dinosaurs – and the Cainozoic ('recent life'). Compared to the empty, unknown eons of the Pre-Cambrian, the Paleozoic was a more limited 400 million years. In sequence during this era there arose the first creatures with external skeletons, the first fishes and the first amphibians, fish-like creatures that learned to colonize the rich sediments left behind by receding seas. Plants evolved to make increasingly good use of the power of the sun and colonized the land. Gradually the first horsetails, leafless shrubs and ferns gave rise to more efficient seed-bearing plants – early spruces, firs and pines. As the forests spread, they were colonized by the first insects, like dragonflies and cockroaches which would be familiar to a time traveler from the twentieth century. Amphibians, which had to moisten their skins regularly and lay their eggs in water, gave way to reptiles, which were independent of the water and laid eggs with tough protective shells on land. In the Permian period which closed the Paleozoic era, 225 million years ago, the reptiles were the dominant large terrestrial creatures.

Miniature Clues to Lost Worlds

Everyone knows of the massive fossil bones that allow scientists to reconstruct dinosaurs. Less well-known are the apparently insignificant fossils that allow researchers to build a wider picture of vanished ages – relics of the plants, trees, and insects that were once some of the myriad elements making up prehistoric environments. The

fossils below, none more than an inch or two in size, are cases in point. They all come from the Stonesfield slate beds which underlie much of Oxfordshire, England. Formed in Jurassic times between 190 and 135 million years ago, they show a mixture of marine and terrestrial life forms, which were swept together by rivers and tides in

the shallow, marshy inlet of the ocean that spread southwards from central England. Some of the life forms from which these fossils derive would seem familiar enough today. Others – like the megalosaur – would certainly not be. One object is of particular interest – the tiny lower jaw of a primitive, mouse-sized mammal.

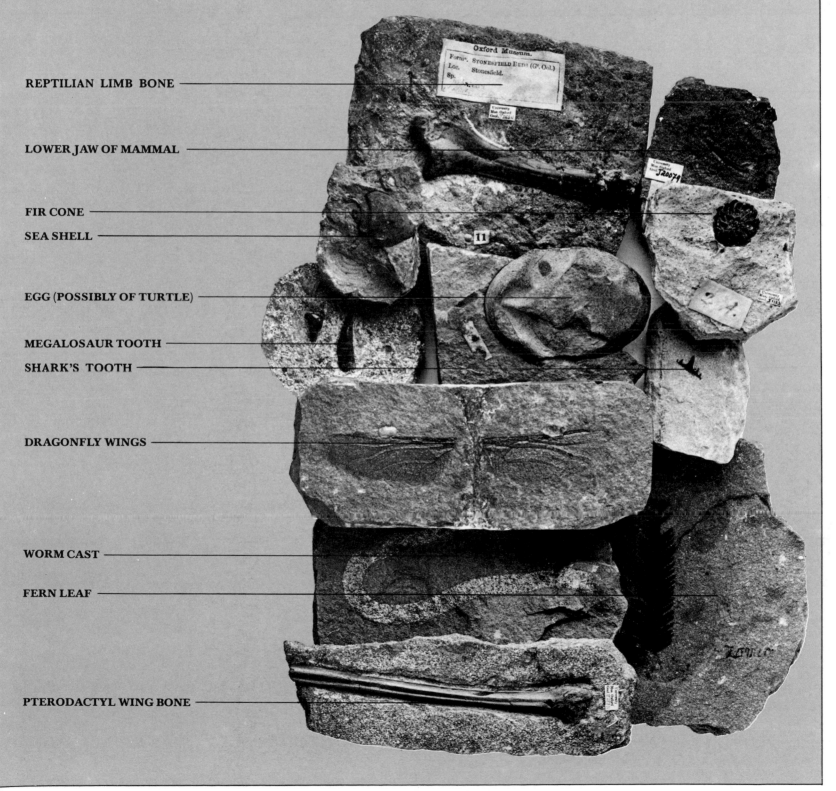

REPTILIAN LIMB BONE

LOWER JAW OF MAMMAL

FIR CONE

SEA SHELL

EGG (POSSIBLY OF TURTLE)

MEGALOSAUR TOOTH

SHARK'S TOOTH

DRAGONFLY WINGS

WORM CAST

FERN LEAF

PTERODACTYL WING BONE

The reptiles had – and still have – a number of advantages over their amphibian predecessors which opened up a new range of possible habitats:

– amphibians have naked skins, without scales, hair, or other protective devices; they are therefore prone to desiccation and must remain near water for their survival. Reptiles evolved a type of horny skin – scales – that prevented drying out.

– where amphibians' eggs are soft and gelatinous and, like the creatures themselves, prone to desiccation, the reptilian egg is built more solidly and absorbs and emits only those gases that are vital to the survival of the unhatched embryo. The egg can be laid anywhere *except* in water.

Thus freed from the need to colonize two environments – water and land – at once, the reptiles began to spread rapidly. From the early carnivores that preyed on each other and more primitive creatures, the first herbivorous reptiles developed. It may seem odd that animals were only secondarily herbivorous – odd, because many food chains now start with plants, which feed plant-eaters, which feed carnivores. But it seems likely that new types of

At the beginning of the Triassic period, 225 million years ago, the mammal-like reptiles were the dominant terrestrial land-forms. Among them were two flesh-eaters, *Cynognathus* (above) and *Thrinaxodon*, (below) transitional between reptiles and mammals. They may well have possessed a furry coat as shown here. They certainly had efficient jaws: reptilian jaws move only up and down but the jaws of the mammal-like reptiles could move backwards, forwards and sideways, which allowed them to chew and digest their food efficiently.

The Earthy Art of Fossil-Hunting

Paleontologists are often asked: 'How do you know where to dig?' In fact, for dinosaur hunters, choice is limited. Most fossils lie in sedimentary rock, that is, rock formed under water. Since dinosaurs were land animals, the most likely place to look for dinosaur skeletons is in rock formed in shallow water – along former coasts lines, in estuaries or shallow lakes where the creatures may have once fed (although some finds, like the iguanodons of Bernissart, may by chance be unearthed at great depths). In addition, it is usually worth searching only where sediments of the right age have been exposed by erosion – on mountain sides, river banks, or coasts.

Once a fossil is found, its exact position is recorded. Every individual particle of bone is given a number. In this way, dating can be done accurately and scientists have a better chance of putting together what would otherwise be a chaotic jigsaw of bones.

Soft bones can be hardened with resin and set in plaster of Paris, like broken limbs. Plaster is laid on in impregnated strips of hessian and after half an hour or so, when the plaster has set, the block is under-mined, lifted over carefully and cleaned on the reverse side. The plastering is then completed.

Sometimes, fossils are found in nodules of hard rock which have to be chipped around and large fossils may demand a pneumatic drill, trucks and construction gear to remove and transport.

After retrieval, come the problems of reconstruction. First, the plaster must be stripped off. Then the rock must be hammered, chiseled, drilled, brushed and even picked away with needles that will remove rock particles one grain at a time. This is long and tiring work and when possible scientists use acid baths to dissolve away the surrounding rock. The results can be extraordinary: a 200 million year old fossil can be restored as neatly as if the animal had died the day before.

Removing bone in Lesotho, Southern Africa.

Plastering ichthyosaur bone, central England.

Plastering near completion.

Excavating footprints, Swanage, England.

Transporting footprint slabs to museum.

animal would have been more likely to eat other animals than plants, because meat is a more efficient way of packaging energy. Newly evolving carnivores, however, faced one insuperable problem: there were only limited amounts of other animals. But plants, even at this stage in the earth's history were virtually unlimited. Here lay a huge evolutionary potential which, once realized, would support countless new species.

As food sources, plants present certain problems. They are difficult to digest and have to be kept in the stomach a long time until they are broken down by bacteria. A great deal of vegetation has to be eaten to match the energy derived from meat. Thus herbivores tended to be rather large and heavy by comparison with carnivores, a tendency that also served as a defense. In response, the carnivores evolved larger forms themselves. Fairly rapidly, therefore, evolutionary pressures produced a complete range of reptilians colonizing a wide range of niches (a niche is a combination of characteristics – food sources, climate, water supply for instance – that offers a way of life to a suitably adapted species. Niches exist whether or not creatures evolve to fill them).

From the early reptiles there developed three main branches in the evolutionary tree: modern reptiles, the dinosaurs and – of particular significance for our species – the mammals, which derived from transitional creatures known as mammal-like reptiles.

For 100 million years, the mammal-like reptiles had the land virtually to themselves. They were, in some ways, more physiologically efficient creatures than the first reptiles. For one thing, they had three distinct types of teeth, as we do. They had canines – a pointed stabbing tooth for attacking prey; incisors for biting off pieces of food; and cheek teeth for chewing. They could thus kill, eat and digest their food more efficiently – an indication that they were probably much more active than any earlier animals.

It could be that they needed to be. One paleontologist has suggested that the late Permian period was a cold time. If it was, any increased activity would have been an advantage in keeping up body temperature. It has also been suggested that some of the mammal-like reptiles had fur, or fat, as a sort of insulation. Useful as this may have been, for true evolutionary success it needed to be balanced by a complementary physiological ability – to lose heat. This may be where the mammal-like reptiles lost out.

The possibility that they had trouble with temperature control is suggested by one of the early mammal-like reptiles, *Dimetrodon*, which had a set of spines sticking up from its backbone forming the skeleton of what was presumably a sail-like appendage. When the creature was first found by Cope, towards the turn of the century, he even suggested that it *was* a sail: the creature could have drifted effortlessly through the shallows, he implied, heeling over gently in the breeze (although it had neither keel nor boom to trim its sail). Another extraordinary suggestion was that the spines were mock reeds which would

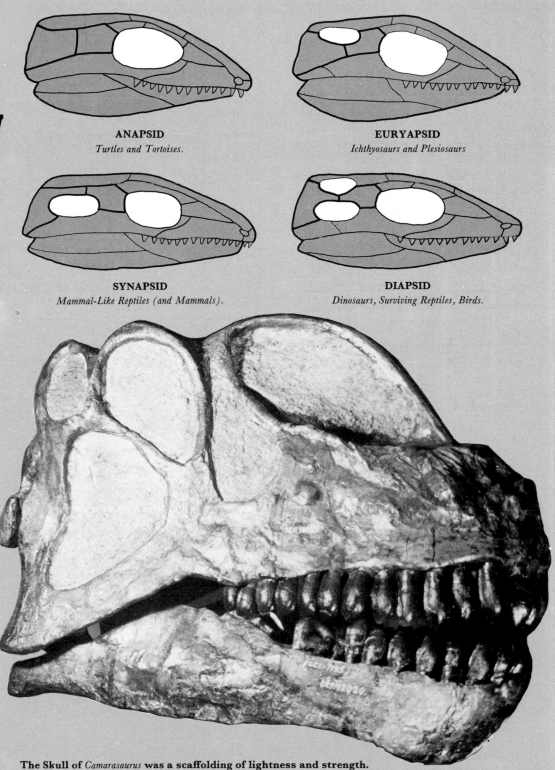

Holes in the Head: A Guide to Reptilian Ancestry

There are four basic skull patterns for all the reptiles in the world, living and extinct. The simplest – solid bone with holes only for the eyes and nostrils – is called the anapsid condition. It was developed by the early amphibians and is retained by many amphibians today.

The other three designs – synapsids, euryapsids and diapsids – all have holes in the temple, on each side behind the eye. Synapsids have a lower opening. Euryapsids, which are all extinct – the design was evolved by ichthyosaurs and plesiosaurs for a sea-dwelling existence – have an upper opening. And the diapsids, with two or more openings, include the dinosaurs and their surviving off-shoots – lizards, snakes, crocodiles and birds, and the uniquely primitive lizard-like tuatara of New Zealand.

Such fenestrations serve two purposes: they combine lightness with strength. The diapsid condition, found in the earliest dinosaurs, allowed for stronger jaw muscles and lighter skulls. The condition evolved in some dinosaurs to create a number of holes scattered around the head until the skull became a veritable lace-work.

ANAPSID
Turtles and Tortoises.

EURYAPSID
Ichthyosaurs and Plesiosaurs

SYNAPSID
Mammal-Like Reptiles (and Mammals).

DIAPSID
Dinosaurs, Surviving Reptiles, Birds.

The Skull of *Camarasaurus* **was a scaffolding of lightness and strength.**

Life's Grand Design: Dinosaurs in Perspective

This diagram sets out a simplified version of life on earth, with particular emphasis on the dinosaurs and, to add a sense of proportion, on man. As a species and as cultured beings (top right) our life is brief indeed in comparison with the 140-million-year rule of the dinosaurs.

The formation of the earth occurred some 4500 million years ago. For over 2000 million years – half the earth's life span – there was no life. Gradually, as if in some massive test tube, chemical reactions powered by lightning and the sun's ultra-violet radiation created the chemical building blocks of living matter. Organic compounds linked successively into self-duplicating molecules, single-celled creatures and the first life forms. These – sponges, jellyfish, coral and many kinds of worm – left no fossil record. The evolution of the first crustacea, 570 million years ago, provided the first major evidence of life.

During the Paleozoic ('early life'), the arthropods – creatures with jointed legs, and bodies partially encased in a shell – expanded rapidly. Fishes also began to evolve at this time.

The Mesozoic ('middle life') was the age of the dinosaurs. The amphibians and the mammal-like reptiles which had dominated the land in previous ages largely died out, and the archosaurs – the technical name for the ruling reptiles, a term which includes the dinosaurs – underwent tremendous expansion (for details see pages 86–87).

Their almost total disappearance at the end of the Mesozoic – the only surviving archosaurs are the crocodilians – presented the mammals and birds with a mass of evolutionary niches to be filled and exploited. Only at the end of this last period – the Cenozoic era – did one tiny branch of the mammals produce the upright, naked ape known as *Homo sapiens*.

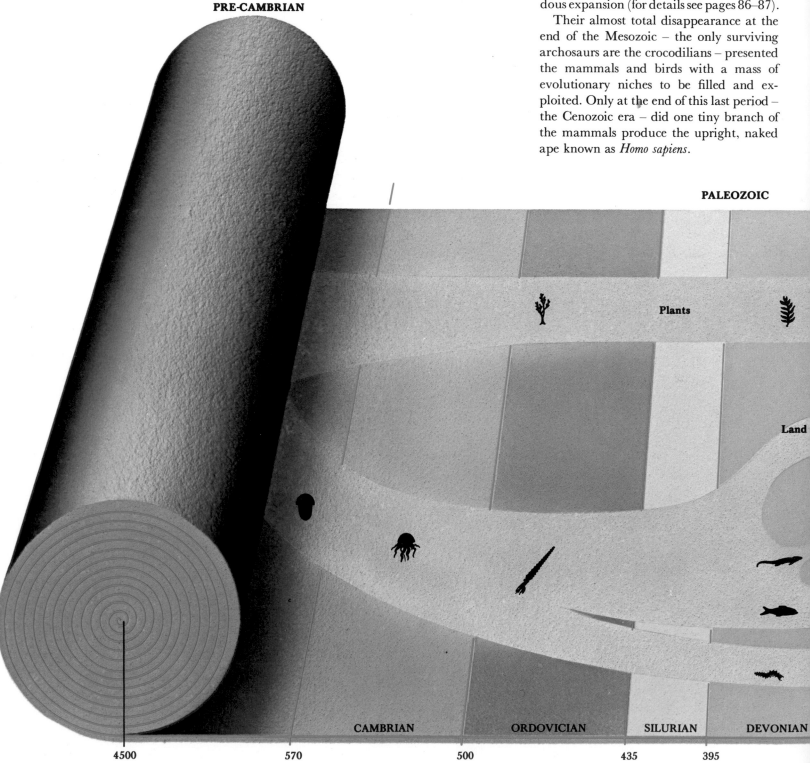

PRE-CAMBRIAN

PALEOZOIC

Plants

Land

CAMBRIAN   ORDOVICIAN   SILURIAN   DEVONIAN

4500   570   500   435   395

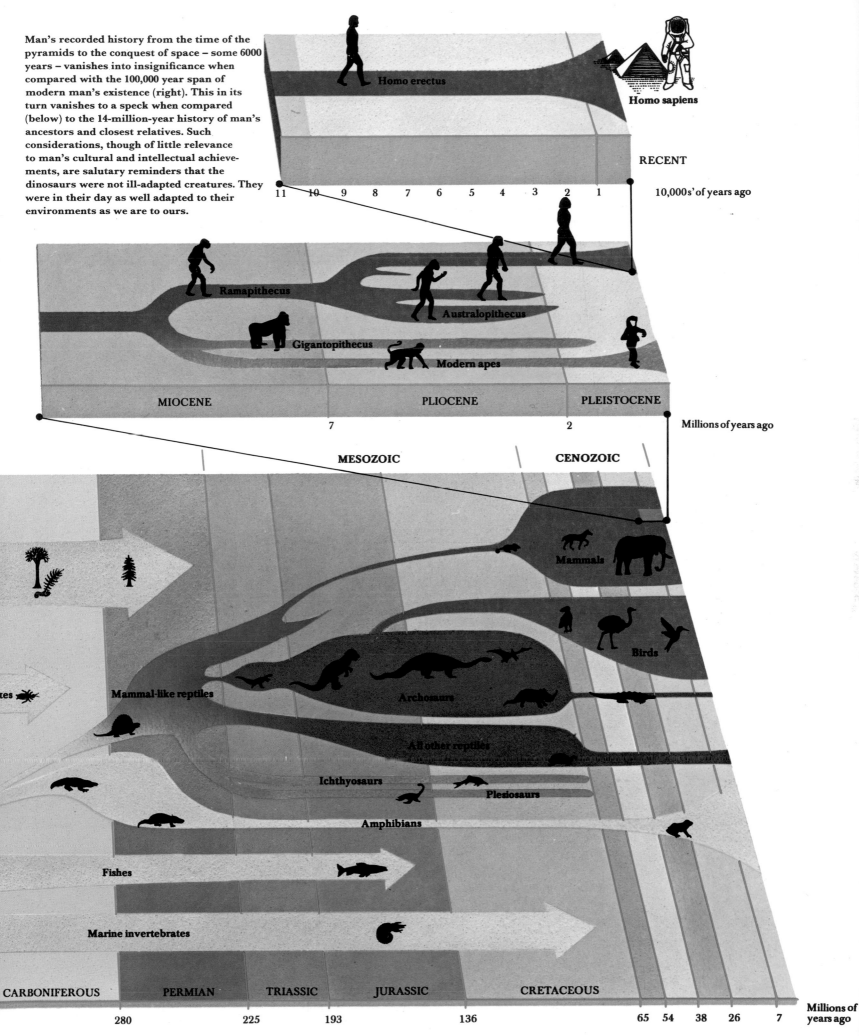

Man's recorded history from the time of the pyramids to the conquest of space – some 6000 years – vanishes into insignificance when compared with the 100,000 year span of modern man's existence (right). This in its turn vanishes to a speck when compared (below) to the 14-million-year history of man's ancestors and closest relatives. Such considerations, though of little relevance to man's cultural and intellectual achievements, are salutary reminders that the dinosaurs were not ill-adapted creatures. They were in their day as well adapted to their environments as we are to ours.

Homo erectus

Homo sapiens

RECENT

11 10 9 8 7 6 5 4 3 2 1   10,000s' of years ago

Ramapithecus

Australopithecus

Gigantopithecus

Modern apes

MIOCENE

PLIOCENE

PLEISTOCENE

7

2

Millions of years ago

MESOZOIC

CENOZOIC

Mammals

Birds

Mammal-like reptiles

Archosaurs

All other reptiles

Ichthyosaurs

Plesiosaurs

Amphibians

Fishes

Marine invertebrates

CARBONIFEROUS PERMIAN TRIASSIC JURASSIC CRETACEOUS

280   225   193   136   65 54 38 26 7

Millions of years ago

55

have disguised the creature when it took cover in long grass. In fact it seems more likely that the sail would have supported skin amply supplied with blood vessels and that the whole thing was thus a sort of a heat-exchanger to absorb and radiate heat, balancing the creature's internal temperature. As a meat eater, *Dimetrodon* might have found it very useful to reach an active temperature early in the morning when its reptilian prey were sluggish and to remain active at midday when other reptiles had to seek out shade and remain quiescent.

Later mammal-like reptiles dropped this sail, experimenting perhaps with other methods of balancing their internal heat. They also developed other less reptilian – and more mammalian – features, like powerful jaw muscles and a bony partition in the roof of the mouth that enabled them to continue eating while breathing, instead of having to stop breathing in order to swallow as some other reptiles do.

But whatever they did right in evolutionary terms, it was not sufficient to rival the great reptiles. The mammal-like reptiles survived only by colonizing the very smallest niches and when traces of them re-emerge – as mammals – they are minute creatures, seldom bigger than rats.

Why were they not immediately successful? The answer must lie in their body chemistry, about which we can only make an informed guess, by looking at the physiology of extremely primitive mammalian creatures – monotremes, for instance, like the Australian spiny ant-eater and the duck-billed platypus, which seem to be specialized survivors from the last of the mammal-like reptiles. They are well insulated against the cold but cannot lose body heat and must remain in their burrows during the heat of the day because their activity might otherwise generate more heat than they can dissipate. They do not pant or perspire as more advanced mammals do.

During the Triassic period, there may have been a steady increase in temperature. Large mammal-like reptiles were ill-equipped for such conditions. Larger creatures do not radiate heat so effectively as small ones, for two reasons:

- larger creatures cannot avoid heat so easily by burrowing or hiding in the shade.
- the larger the creature, the more bulk there is in relation to the surface area. In other words there is more of them on the inside (which is why a baby loses heat quicker than an adult and needs to be wrapped up more).

To survive the growing heat, therefore, the mammal-like reptiles had to become small. They 'elected' to balance their high temperatures and good insulation by evolving as diminutive creatures which were good heat radiators and which could rapidly burrow away from the tropical surface. Hence the fact that the mammals evolved first as shrew-like creatures.

Of the other two lines that evolved from the early reptiles, one (the modern reptiles) is of only marginal interest here; the other forms the subject of this book. This third line evolved into a number of types known collectively as the archosaurs, or 'ruling reptiles.' They arose in the very late Permian, some 225 million years ago, and evolved for the next 30 million years as a steadily expanding group known as the thecodonts. These gave rise to four major groups: the crocodiles, the birds, the flying reptiles and the dinosaurs.

The thecodonts were a completely new type of creature, as their name – which means 'socket tooth' – implies. Their teeth were not, as is the case with lizards, fused to the jaw but were individually rooted and could therefore be individually replaced. Another specialty that must have set them apart from their mammal-like contemporaries was an ability to lose heat. They almost certainly had no insulation – fat, fur or feathers.

In the Middle Triassic something extraordinary happened: the thecodonts inherited the earth. The changeover from the old-style creatures to the new is dramatic. The old-style amphibians and reptiles had survived well enough for 150 million years but against the stronger thecondontian competition they stood little chance in most of the major habitats.

Why?

Look at the earlier creatures again: they were sprawlers, sustaining themselves in a 'push-up' position, which meant that they could not run very efficiently. Their mode of locomotion was a sort of serpentine waddle. None of them became bipedal, none of them climbed trees as far as we know, very few burrowed, none were heavily armored, they did not grow particularly large – no bigger than horse size – none of them returned completely to the water (though some were semi-aquatic) and none took to the air.

The thecondonts and their descendants, by comparison, sound like evolutionary paragons. They tucked their limbs underneath them, which gave them better support and greater speed. Some could sprint on their toes. Soon, some learned to raise their front feet off the ground and achieved greater speed yet. They evolved types of all sizes, from goose-sized light-weights to 80-ton giants. Many had highly specialized dentition. They took to the air *twice*, once as flying reptiles and the second time with better insulation – feathers – and thus originated the birds. Whole lines of them recolonized the water, so successfully (the ichthyosaurs looked remarkably

Walking Tall: A Key to Dinosaurian Success

The archosaurs, the group to which the dinosaurs belong, rose to dominance during the Triassic largely because they evolved a more efficient gait. Dinosaur ancestors (left) were salamander-like. They meandered along in an energy-consuming press-up position, resting frequently. Many thecodontians – the dinosaurs' immediate predecessors – had a crocodile stance (center), suitable for no more than a quick sprint. Dinosaurs however (right) evolved with underslung legs. They could support themselves without effort, and run fast and far – a prerequisite for a two-legged gait.

YOUNGINA, LATE PERMIAN   **MANDASUCHUS, MIDDLE TRIASSIC**   **ORNITHOSUCHUS, LATE TRIASSIC**

The Drifting Continents: Rafts for Reptilian Giants

The world of the dinosaurs was very different from today's world. Several hundred million years ago, the continents – riding like rafts on the back of surging currents of rock – were ground together to form one single land mass known as Pangaea ('land everywhere'). This meant that the early dinosaurs could colonize any suitable habitat anywhere on earth. Identical fossils have been found in places now separated by thousands of miles of sea. One dinosaurian predecessor, *Lystrosaurus*, has been found in South Africa, India and Antarctica. Experts expect similar fossils to turn up in South America and Australia.

Two hundred million years ago, Pangaea began to break up. At first it separated into two super-continents, Laurasia and Gondwanaland, along the line of the Tethys Sea, the ancestral Mediterranean. Gradually dinosaur families on the separate continental plates evolved new and individualistic species, especially in the south. But in the north, North America and Asia remained connected across the North Atlantic and dinosaurs like *Tyrannosaurus* and the horned species migrated between the two continents. Many late Cretaceous species, therefore, show only marginal differences in the two areas.

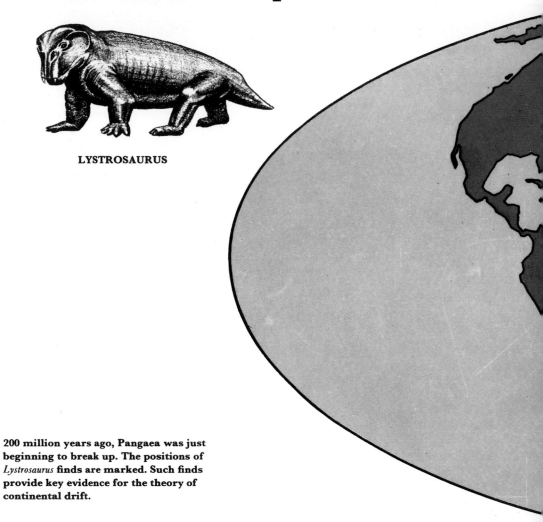

LYSTROSAURUS

200 million years ago, Pangaea was just beginning to break up. The positions of *Lystrosaurus* **finds are marked. Such finds provide key evidence for the theory of continental drift.**

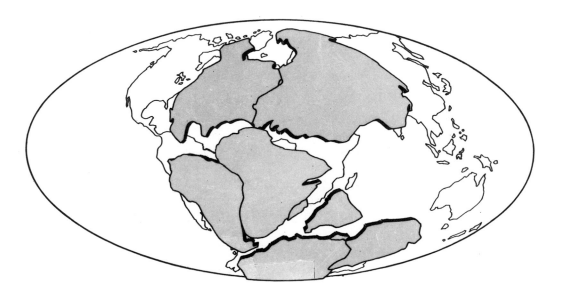

180 million years ago, Pangaea had split into Laurasia and Gondwanaland, which had itself begun to break into its constituent parts. India was already driving northwards from Africa towards Asia.

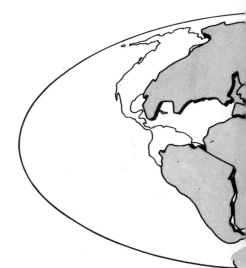

135 million years ago, drift was continuing, with South America beginning to separate from Africa to form a primitive South Atlantic. Australia and Antarctica were still joined, and there was, perhaps, a tiny land bridge across the Straits of Gibraltar.

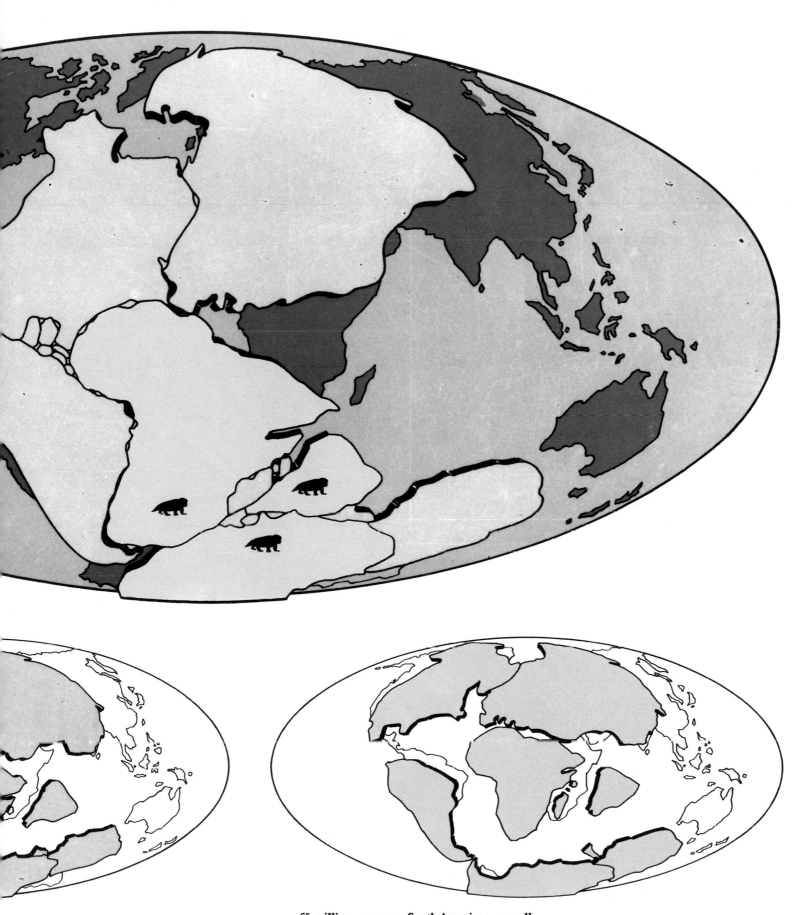

65 million years ago, South America was well clear of Africa but Australia and Antarctica were still joined, as were North America and Europe.

like modern dolphins) that they never had to go on land at all.

Why did this happen? No one knows all the answers, but Alan Charig, of the British Museum (Natural History) in London, has suggested that the invention of the upright gait – the 'fully improved' posture as he calls it – had a number of vital consequences. Any species that walked with a more 'improved' posture could run faster, and thus be better equipped to prey on the mammal-like reptiles. Once the first thecodontian carnivores had done this, they found themselves in the midst of a positive cornucopia. They could literally feed on anything that moved. Within a few million years, they would have eaten themselves to an evolutionary standstill. But there was also a whole new world to be colonized – that occupied by the herbivores upon which they were preying. In the course of time these new advanced creatures learned to eat plants, which in its turn led to new specializations. Evolutionary pressure was for a time intense. Odd mutations conferred unexpected advantages to individuals and the changes were rapidly passed on to descendants, forming new species. By the end of the Triassic, the thecodonts – or the dinosaurs and other related groups as they now were – were truly the ruling reptiles.

If we accept this, it leads on to the more specialized question of why the thecondents evolved an upright gait. But before we get to that, pause a moment while we examine a question of more general – if equally vital significance.

What sort of world did the thecodonts and their declining contemporaries the mammal-like reptiles, inhabit? To answer that question involves a sweeping theory about the nature of the earth and its past – the theory of continental drift, which has revolutionized the science of geology over the past 20 years. It is equivalent in its implications to the revolution of the mid-nineteenth century initiated by Charles Darwin's writings on evolution. In brief the arguments behind this change of thinking are as follows:

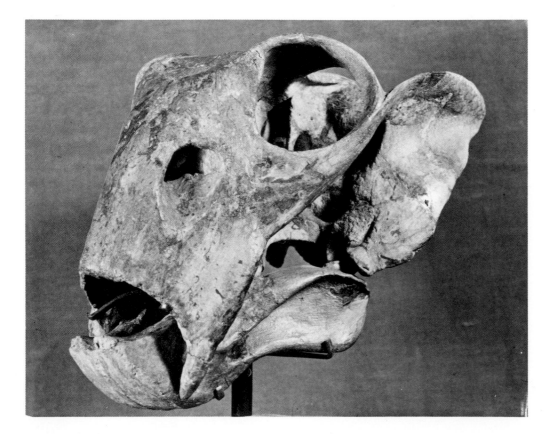

Lystrosaurus **was a four-foot reptile, solidly built as this skull suggests, which roamed widely in the southern hemisphere in early Triassic times. It probably occupied the niche of a small hippopotamus, wallowing in rivers and lakes.**

Until the 1950s most geologists considered the earth to be a stable ball of rock, gradually cooling down. As it cooled, it shrank, and as it shrank its skin wrinkled, forming mountains, lowering ocean floors and raising land bridges that occasionally linked the continents. In this way they could devise a superficially convincing explanation for the existence of marine fossils inland and for mountain-building processes. There were problems of course – why, for instance, were the effects of compression limited to long, linear belts, rather than being evenly distributed? And why should mountains arise in bursts? But generally most scientists could have agreed with the geologist Eduard Suess who in 1900 wrote dramatically: 'What we are witnessing is the collapse of the world.'

Yet a number of scientists were bothered by the deficiencies in the contraction theory. The fact that the world's land masses could be fitted roughly together like a giant jigsaw puzzle seemed just too much of a coincidence. The theory that the continents had actually shifted apart was first proposed by a German, Alfred Wegener, in the first decades of this century. He took seriously a thought that had been common to countless amateur speculators before him, namely that the coasts of North America and South America matched quite remarkably the coast lines of Europe and Africa. They must, he said, have once been together. He suggested that the continents were light granitic rock plates floating on denser basaltic rock. But Wegener could propose no mechanism by which these movements had taken place, and scientists were easily able to make fun of him because the match was not exact.

Now we know that Wegener was right. The earth is *not* stable. It is only our limited life-span that allows us to consider it so. We should see it rather as a ball of hot putty, cooler towards the surface, with slabs of thin stone floating on its surface. These slabs are the continents. From the white hot interior of the earth, currents of molten rock well up like molasses towards the cooler surface. As they reach the surface, these currents veer to either side and slide along the surface of the earth before plunging back into the depths again. At the surface, these currents bear along with them the floating slabs of continental rock. The continents and the plates that form their foundations, shifting a fraction of an inch every year – one or two feet a century – collide. In collision, they throw up mountains, create earthquakes and form volcanic strips. The match between the continental plates is remarkably exact – if the continental shelves rather than the present-day coast lines are taken as the true boundaries.

This process, it is assumed, has continued since the formation of the continents, though how many times the world's land masses may have collided and divided will perhaps never be known. Certainly there are remnants of mountains that are very ancient indeed, however. The Urals, now worn to mere bumps by hundreds of millions of years of erosion, were once the towering products of a collision between Europe and Asia. The worn down hillocks of the eastern seaboard of the United States are the remnants of towering ranges formed in some primeval collision between North America and Europe.

The description of these extended earth movements usually begins some 220 million years ago, when all the land masses of the earth were joined together in a massive super-continent known as Pangaea ('land every-where'). This was the world in which the thecodonts evolved.

The previous few million years had suited the mammal-like reptiles because the world was almost uniformly mild. The North Pole was not cut off by land as it is now, nor were there any large land masses over either Pole. Antarctica was well up towards the tropics. Ocean currents thus circulated freely, preventing the formation of polar ice caps that have – over the last two million years, for instance – been the cause of a number of extended cold spells, or ice ages.

There is considerable geological evidence now for the once uniform nature of the earth's land masses. But reptiles also play their part in the evidence. In Permian times for instance, there was a two-foot long aquatic reptile, *Mesosaurus*, with paddle-like limbs and needle-like teeth, that inhabited both South America and South Africa. In both Czechoslovakia and Texas, fossil hunters have found remains of a weird and unmistakable creature, *Edaphosaurus*, which had spines all along its back on which were short horizontal cross bars. But the best evidence of all concerns a heavily-built mammal-like reptile, *Lystrosaurus*, with a large body, short, stout legs, a stumpy tail and two tusks jutting out of its blunt nose on either side of a beak which it used for nibbling at tough water plants. *Lystrosaurus* fossils occur so abundantly in some sediments under-lying the surface of South Africa that they have been named the *Lystrosaurus* zone. Indeed some 85% of all the fossils there are *Lystrosaurus*. But *Lystrosaurus* fossils are also found in India, in China, and most significantly in Antarctica – proof positive that 200 million years ago Antarctica, India and South Africa were all joined in a vast tropical or subtropical land.

At this time Pangaea was beginning to break up. The northern and southern land masses split into two continents, known as Laurasia and Gondwanaland which were divided by the great ocean of Tethys, running westwards through the Panama isthmus, and eastwards acrosss a marine region of which the Mediterranean is a tiny remnant.

Pangaea has continued to break up ever since. A hundred million years ago – that is after 100 million years of drift – South America had almost separated from Africa and off the east coast of Africa, India was migrating northwards, towards Asia. In the south, Antarctica and Australia were still linked in one large land mass. Towards the end of the dinosaur era, 75 million years ago, North America had just separated from Europe and the other major land masses were pretty much on their own. They are still on the move, as any earthquake testifies. A few million years hence, California will have split

Desmatosuchus was a heavily armored crocodile-like representative of a group of reptiles, contemporary to and related to the first dinosaurs. This group, theaetosaurs, were rapidly made extinct by their more efficient dinosaurian cousins.

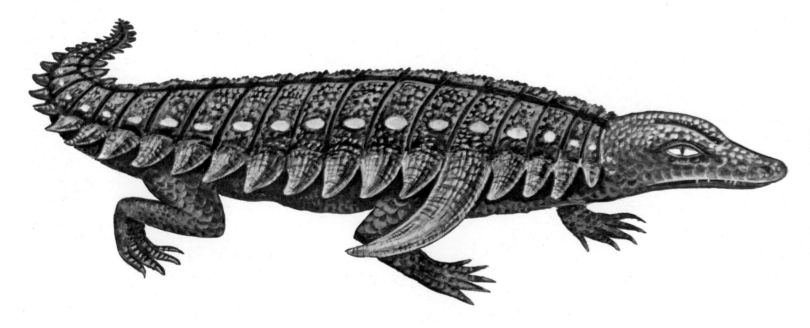

apart from the rest of America along the San Andreas Fault and much of East Africa will be on its way towards India, having split along the Great Rift Valley.

All this is vital for an understanding of the archosaurian fauna. It explains why some species were spread over a very wide area and why in later times, other species lived an isolated existence. It also partially explains why the dinosaurs arose and were successful; and, as we shall see, it partly accounts for their extinction as well.

At the beginning of the Triassic, 225 million years ago, the mammal-like reptiles still ruled supreme. Their days were numbered, however. Creeping on to the evolutionary stage were the first thecodonts. They would have seemed unexceptional creatures. They looked very much like crocodiles. In fact they ultimately gave rise to crocodiles and any modern crocodile gives a good idea of what the first thecodonts looked like – sluggish for much of the time, semi-aquatic to help in keeping cool, sprawling, yet able to move quite rapidly when necessary.

The best known of the early thecodonts – the first true archosaurs – was a crocodilian-like creature called *Proterosuchus*. It was only about five feet long but it had a powerful battery of teeth and spent its life swimming in the shallows, where it hunted for fish, and waddling on the shores on its sprawling legs, where it probably fed on its contemporary, *Lystrosaurus*. The descendants

The fossil footprints of *Cheirotherium* look somewhat like the imprints of a human hand. They are about the same size, but the 'thumb' was in fact the fifth digit – the little finger or toe which stuck out sideways. Though its name means 'hand-mammal', its tracks, with left and right feet planted just a few inches apart, show that its legs moved in a vertical plane (unlike *Desmatosuchus*, left). Though its pedigree is uncertain, it may have been an early dinosaur.

This composite scene shows the variety of creatures whose fossils have been retrieved from one small area – around Elgin and Lossiemouth in the county of Moray on the east coast of Scotland. On the ground, are primitive forms of reptile that inhabited Scotland in the Permian, up to 225 million years ago. On the rock above are successor species, early dinosaurs of the Triassic. The Permian forms include a *Geikia* (in pool), a northern version of *Lystrosaurus*. Also shown are two *Stagonolepsis*, aetosaurs that survived into the Triassic and were thus contemporary with such species as *Ornithosuchus* (the three individuals at top left), which is often considered the first true dinosaur. Further up the rock are two carnivorous dinosaurs, *Scleromochlus* (left) and the long-tailed *Saltopus*. Below them are two other local reptilian forms, *Erpetosuchus* (with small bony plates on its back) and the little, sprawling, primitive, *Telerpeton*.

of *Proterosuchus* evolved into solid, scaly creatures, some of which could have easily been mistaken for crocodiles (although one major difference was that their nostrils were not – as in crocodiles today – at the end of the snout; they were set in a crater on top of the head, just in front of the eyes).

There were also plant-eating thecodonts of a similar squat four-legged build. But whether carnivorous or herbivorous, these early thecodonts had several things in common: their build, their gait, a scaly armor and, most significant, a flattened tail and powerful back legs to drive them through the water.

The early crocodilians were sprawlers. This is not a gait suitable for a ruling reptile. The thecodonts needed to raise themselves off the ground and develop limbs that were tucked in under their body so that they could move faster and more efficiently. The first animal to achieve this may have been a *Cheirotherium* which means 'hand-mammal.' 'May have been' because the creature itself has never been found; it is known only from its footprints which look remarkably like those of a mammal, with four solid fingers and a 'thumb' that sticks out to the side, apparently just like a human thumb. When the footprints were first discovered in the early nineteenth century, dinosaurs were unknown and it was assumed that the prints were those of an amphibian. The 'thumb' print is in fact that of a little finger which makes it seem as though the 'thumb' is on the 'wrong side.' One scientist, wrestling with this problem, suggested that the beast had actually crossed its legs at each stride. Once this odd notion had been dispensed with it was possible to

EUPARKERIA

ORNITHOSUCHUS

66

make a good guess about the shape of the creature that made the tracks. The creature must have been about nine feet long, it held itself clear of the ground (there are no signs that its tail dragged in the mud) and since the track is only a few inches wide, its limbs must have been held directly underneath its body. The separated little finger was apparently an adaptation to give the creature better grip as it walked.

Three other creatures, which display the change-over from thecodont to dinosaur, offer a better indication of what was to come. The first of these creatures was *Euparkeria*. First described just before the First World War by Robert Broom, the foremost South African paleontologist, *Euparkeria* was a small creature, only two or three feet long, but it was remarkable for the fact that its front legs were much shorter than its back legs and Broom concluded: 'the animal possibly ran on its hind feet' – though it probably dropped down on all fours when walking. He imagined the little creature chasing large insects, like locusts, or dragonflies, and snatching them from the air with its front legs before crunching them up. In the side of *Euparkeria's* snout there was a large opening in the bone which is a distinguishing feature of all the archosaurs (although it has not been retained by crocodiles today). No one knows what the fenestrations were for, although it is possible that they accommodated a salt gland – which lizards have today – but it is anyway a useful distinguishing feature for paleontologists.

The second well known Triassic archosaur was a more advanced version of *Euparkeria*, found in the Elgin sandstone in Scotland in the 1890s, its name highlighted its odd nature. It was called *Ornithosuchus*, the 'bird crocodile.' Up to 12 feet long, it must have been an alert and fast animal that darted about in

These three Triassic reptiles represent the progression and diversification of Triassic species. *Euparkeria*, which evolved about 225 million years ago, grew up to three foot long and could, on occasion, run on its back legs. Its possible descendant, *Ornithosuchus*, which grew up to ten feet in length, was fully bipedal. It was undoubtedly a flesh-eater and probably the ancestor of the great dinosaurian carnivores. Its contemporary, the nimble *Coelophysis*, with its longer tail and smaller head, was also a biped but preyed on much smaller creatures.

COELOPHYSIS

search of small reptiles. It had a mass of sharp, serrated teeth and ran about on its hind legs, using its fore-limbs for walking and for grabbing its prey. The back legs were tucked well under its body and it balanced itself with its tail as it ran.

Ornithosuchus was definitely bipedal. Its thigh-bone pointed straight down, whereas *Euparkeria's* had stuck out to the side at an angle of about 45° and with front-limbs even shorter than *Euparkeria's*, if *Ornithosuchus* had walked on all fours its backbone would have arched uncomfortably over its pelvis. *Ornithosuchus* is recognized as the ancestor of all the large flesh-eating dinosaurs that developed later.

The third group were lightly built graceful creatures that relied principally on their speed for catching their small prey – dragonflies, perhaps, or small newly hatched dinosaurs. A particularly well known species is *Coelophysis* (pronounced See-lo-fie-sis). Individuals were first unearthed in 1881 in New Mexico by David Baldwin. Initially Baldwin was a collector for Marsh but became dissatisfied with his employer, who, he felt, did not recognize the importance of his finds. He therefore transferred his allegiance to Cope.

Baldwin was something of an eccentric. He liked to work in the New Mexican desert in the depths of winter, when he could at least be assured of an adequate water supply. He worked out of the ancient New Mexican town of Abiquiu, near which there were colorful bluffs of rock. In 1881 he shipped off some finds to Cope, describing them as 'small and tender.' Cope promptly announced the discovery of three species of *Coelophysis* ('hollow nature') but for the next 60 years the creature remained something of an enigma. Then in 1947 a party from the American Museum of Natural History, staying at a private home known as Ghost Ranch, found a mass of *Coelophysis* bones, piled on top of one another – heads, tails, feet, legs all mixed together.

Some of the skeletons are complete and rate as some of the most perfect dinosaur skeletons known. They represent all ages, from babies up to adults. The quarry is only 30 feet square and it looks as if whole herds or families were overwhelmed by some disaster – a flood, perhaps. Whatever happened, their deaths were not particularly violent. The creatures were eight or ten feet long when fully grown and yet weighed only 40 or 50 pounds. The bones were delicately made and hollow containing air sacs like the bones of birds, perhaps an adaptation to save weight and increase speed. They had sinuous necks, a long, thin skull and a very long tail, which gave them a racy appearance. They had delicate, saw-toothed teeth, ideal for slicing up flesh quickly. Their hind legs and three-toed feet were remarkably like those of birds.

The Ghost Ranch skeletons pose one as yet unanswered puzzle: within two almost perfect skeletons are the remains of small *Coelophysis* individuals. These may either be the skeletons of unborn young (which assumes that *Coelophysis* gave birth to live young rather than laying eggs), or they might be the results of some cannibalistic feast by the elders (modern crocodiles sometimes eat their young). Both suggestions have their problems. The small skeletons are remarkably large for young. Though some modern lizards do give birth to young that are half the length of the adult, the *Coelophysis's* pelvic opening seems too small to accommodate such youngsters. If they are the results of cannibalism, the skeletons are remarkably unharmed: it seems extraordinary that the little creatures could have been swallowed without a bone being broken. No one as yet knows the answer.

How did the thecodonts and early dinosaurs become bipedal? Why should a creature evolve shorter front legs and longer back legs? There would initially seem to be little advantage for a quadruped to have shorter front legs; it would *decrease* speed, at least until the creatures evolved a two-legged stance. The answer probably lies in the thecodonts' marshy origins, and in the strong back legs and tail developed as aids to swimming. As the climate dried out during the course of the Triassic, these adaptations may have proved useful for species that were forced to adopt a more mobile existence on dry land. Successive species must have found that, by raising themselves on their hind-limbs, they could temporarily shift into top gear and at the same time use their fore-limbs as hands to catch prey. The tail, meanwhile, would have tended to act as a counter-balance to their bodies. Gradually these evolutionary discoveries, in which the adaptations of one mode of life proved advantageous in another, became formalized in a new type creature – a small, fast biped which proved to be the direct descendant of one group of dinosaurs.

The thecodonts, therefore, invented the upright pose – one of the most momentous changes in biological design in the history of the world. They and their successor species could now choose between fast movement over the ground or – on the basis of vertical limbs that supported them without much use of muscular energy – could opt for greater size and ultimately a return to the four-footed stance – an option that eventually led to the huge multi-ton monsters of children's picture books.

The 70-foot, 30-ton *Brontosaurus* is, in the words of one scientist, 'literally Mr Dinosaur himself' for the public at large.

3/The First of the Ruling Reptiles

At the time of the Late Triassic, 200 million years ago, the early dinosaurs were the dominant life-form on land. They had almost completely taken over from the less racily built thecodonts. The mammal-like reptiles had already declined·both in size and variety into insignificance and were represented only by the first mammals, tiny shrew-like creatures – their skulls were only an inch long – filling a niche that they were to occupy obscurely but successfully for the next 135 million years. The dinosaurs, on the other hand, soon began to evolve larger species. Bulk must have conferred considerable benefits, because within a few million years a large number of species were giants by our mammalian terms. Presumably size offered protection against predators, and probably also allowed them to preserve a stable temperature.

Fairly rapidly in evolutionary terms, there emerged a range of dinosaurs which can, for the sake of convenience, be divided into four major types: large and small herbivores, and large and small carnivores. One early plant-eater was discovered by Marsh himself, near Manchester, Connecticut. Marsh called it *Anchisaurus* but it was later renamed *Yaleosaurus* – more suitably perhaps, given Marsh's contribution to that University but an indication of the terminological confusions that beset any dinosaur researcher. *Anchisaurus* (or is it *Yaleosaurus*?) scarcely qualifies as a giant, being only seven or eight feet long but it is clearly a distinctive type – heavy body; short squat limbs; blunt teeth; short jaws.

The best known of these early plant-eaters, however, is called *Plateosaurus*. Measuring up to 20 feet in length, *Plateosaurus* was one of the first dinosaurs to show some bulk. Its broadly arched ribs and bulky stomach gave it a barrel-like appearance. It had stout hind-limbs, broad hind feet, with four strong forward pointing toes. Its fore-limbs were also strong enough to help it in walking and standing but when running and feeding it must have reared itself on its hind-limbs. What it ate is a matter of some dispute. Its teeth were blunt in shape – spatulate, or rounded – ideal for munching up soft vegetation and its long neck and small head were typical of the even bigger plant-eaters that were its probable descendants. But it also had clawed fingers and hands that were turned inwards, as if suitable for catching and holding small prey.

The fact that we know so much about the *Plateosaurus* is due to one of the greatest of paleontologists, Friedrich von Huene, who came from Tübingen in Germany. Von Huene became interested in dinosaurs as a young man and wrote a monograph about Triassic dinosaurs at the turn of the century. Tall, spare and distinguished, he was an aesthetic man who lived humbly on the simplest of diets, who did not drink or smoke. He struck Alan Charig, who stayed with the von Huenes briefly in the 1960s, as positively saintly. He was also a man of incredible energy. Once when he was in his eighties he hiked for three days across Germany to attend a scientific conference. He remained the grand old man of paleontology until his death in 1967, when he was well into his nineties. He thus bridged two eras in the history of dinosaur hunting.

Von Huene was well placed to study the earliest dinosaurs, for central Germany possessed three distinctive groups of sedimentary rocks that gave their name to the whole Triassic (or Trias – a group of three – as it was originally called). The upper strata of these rocks – the Keuper beds – were widely known as excellent for fossil finds by the mid-nineteenth century. Some particularly large heavy bones had been named *Plateosaurus* by 1837. It was von Huene's ambition to find complete skeletons of Triassic dinosaurs. In the summer of 1921 he succeeded on a sloping hillside overlooking farmland in a wooded valley, near Trossingen, 30 miles from Tübingen. A quarry was excavated by scores of students and technicians under von Huene's super-vision. The quarriers inched their way deep into the hill side, following the Keuper beds. Thousands of bones – almost all of them belonging to *Plateosaurus* – were collected, meticulously mapped, hardened, coated in plaster of Paris and shipped back to von Huene's museum. The material allowed von Huene to create a detailed description of *Plateosaurus* and its way of life.

During the Late Triassic in what is now central Europe, there seems to have been a wide belt of desert separating high land on the east and an inland sea – later to become part of the Tethys – to the west, while the coast lay further south. There were, von Huene suggested, two seasons, wet and dry, as

Friedrich von Huene – spare, dignified and active until well into his 90s – unearthed numerous skeletons of *Plateosaurus* (below), one of the best known Triassic dinosaurs and a predecessor of the giant herbivores.

in the tropics now. The plateosaurs would sensibly escape to the hills in the wet season, and migrate down to the lake in herds six months later. Their 80-mile march took them across the desert strip. As they plodded along, the weak, young and sickly would fall and die. Their bodies were buried by wind-blown sand, entombed and fossilized until revealed by von Huene and his army of earnest students. So monumental was his achievement, that when a very similar find was made in China, several years later, it was named in his honor.

The Late Triassic also saw the emergence of another type of plant-eater: miniature creatures only three feet long. These were a radically different sort of dinosaur, with a hip structure that sets them way apart from the reptilian types from which they evolved. For the moment, however, it's best not to go into the technical differences – that question deserves a section on its own.

The second group of dinosaurs that were already common in Late Triassic times were powerful predatory meat-eaters.

Typical of the early carnosaurs was *Teratosaurus*. Although nowhere near as fearsome as the later giant carnivores, it was still a sizeable 20 foot long and must have weighed perhaps half a ton. Its neck was fairly short, its back legs bulky, with a long tail to counter-balance its heavy body. It had the three-toed feet that all the later carnosaurs had. Its heavy hook-like claws – one on each hand – were perhaps adaptations for grasping or slashing prey. It had a large heavy skull furnished with vicious blade-like teeth. On the basis of the

fragmentary finds attributed to the beast, one dinosaur expert, Edwin Colbert, has described it imaginatively as 'a truly formidable creature, walking with somewhat ponderous tread across the primitive landscape, its large head carried high in a searching look for its prey, its white teeth gleaming in long jaws, its thick leathery skin clothing the body with a strong, flexible protective armor'.

A fourth group of dinosaurs were the light-weight, swift meat-eaters like *Coelophysis*. But it is a fair guess that the trackways studied by Hitchcock in Massachusetts in the early nineteenth century were those of so-called coelurosaurs ('hollow hinder-part lizards'). These creatures must have sprinted about the Triassic lowlands in profusion, seeking insects and other small creatures which they snatched up with their prehensile hands and razor-sharp jaws.

These four types gave an idea of the growing variety of dinosaurs that emerged in the Late Triassic as the single huge continent of Pangaea began to break up. It is now time to pause and provide a framework within which these various types and their even more varied descendants can be understood. Here we step on to uncertain ground, for the classification of dinosaurs has been a matter of intense scientific debate since Owen first suggested the term Dinosauria.

The basic unit with which classifiers work is the species. Traditionally a species is the smallest 'unit' of relationship. Creatures of one species – however varied – can interbreed; creatures of different species cannot (or rather *do* not, or would not if they were alive, although if they are reasonably closely related they can be made to do so as is the case with lions and tigers). If a species is regarded as a twig on the tree of life and each twig is joined to successively larger units, the larger twigs, branches and boughs are given names that roughly indicate the relationships between the various types of creature. Species are thus grouped into genera, which are grouped successively into families, orders, classes, phyla and kingdoms (of which there are two: plants and animals). The initial letters of this vital sequence can easily be recalled with the following mnemonic: 'Sexy Girls From Oklahoma Cuddle Prior to Kissing.' These groupings however, offer only a rough guide because all of them can be further subdivided, although such complexities are generally reserved for the world of today when the animals can be observed in all their baffling complexity.

Owen had rather vaguely suggested that Dinosauria be regarded as a 'distinct tribe or sub-order' of reptiles. He therefore implied that he thought

Plateosaurus, 20 foot long, had solid forelimbs that suggest it was partly quadrupedal (as here) but they were also short, which suggests that it would rear up on two legs to browse on high bushes and trees.

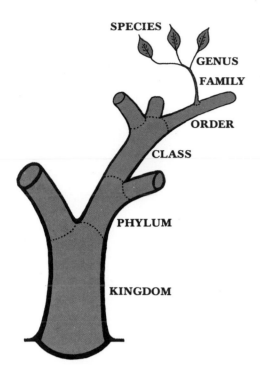

This diagram shows the major units used by scientists to classify any species and relate it to the 'tree of life.'

that all dinosaurs would be closely related as different genera in the same order. Various other suggestions were made soon after by Huxley, Marsh and Cope. Cope placed great emphasis on the bones of the lower leg, Marsh on the sum of differing characteristics, Huxley on the degree to which species seemed to resemble birds. But in 1887 a fundamental distinction was suggested by Harry Govier Seeley, who remained an independent researcher and author until quite late in life, when he was appointed a Professor at London University. Seeley pointed out that all the known dinosaurs could be divided into two types as defined by their hip bones. Some – the saurischians, or lizard-hipped types – possessed a long pubis, that pointed almost straight down; the other sort – the ornithischians, or bird-hipped types – had a pubis that had a short branch directed forwards and a thin rod-like branch directed obliquely downwards and backwards.

It is still generally accepted that Seeley's division is a valid one, because the two types of hips involve a number of other basic differences in skeletal structure. The Saurischia, for instance (which may have developed first) have abdominal ribs; and the ornithischians possess tendons to support the tail. The effects of these differences between them can be summarized as follows: the Saurischia were the carnivorous bipeds and the gigantic herbivorous quadrupeds; the Ornithischia also included both bipeds and quadrupeds but they were all herbivorous and the quadrupeds were all protected in some way with armor, horns, or spikes.

The reasons for this great division are not known for sure but in 1972 Alan Charig of the British Museum (Natural History) suggested an explanation. He analyzed the gait of the major evolutionary groups leading to dinosaurs – the sprawling reptiles, the thecodonts with their more efficient, semi-erect pose and the 'fully improved' vertical stance of the two types of dinosaurs. He argued that the process by which the femurs or thigh-bones tended to be set increasingly in a vertical plane in the course of several million years of evolution had an effect upon the structure of the creature's hips. To understand this relationship demands something of a backtrack.

The advantages of a fully vertical stance are numerous. Compare, for instance, the gait of a lizard with that of a greyhound. A lizard with limbs that stick out horizontally before turning at the elbow through 90° towards the ground, must expend energy just to get off the ground. For a lizard to stand it has to do a push-up which even for mammals like us is a notoriously difficult pose to sustain. Secondly in order to walk the legs have to be swung in arcs which means that the backbone must be swung back and forth in S-shaped curves – a cumbersome and inefficient mode of movement.

In the upright gait little muscular energy is needed to stand. Almost all of it can go into the business of moving. The more vertical a creature is therefore the better it moves. Moreover the backbone freed from the need to wriggle from side to side, can act now as a spring to take up the strain of motion and can make its own contribution. When a mammal, like a greyhound, runs the backbone acts as a spring to increase the length of stride.

In an evolutionary response to these facts of life the thecodonts were 'semi-improved' like modern crocodiles. Their thighs pointed downwards at 45–50°, a big improvement on the horizontal position of their reptilian predecessors. In this pose they still had to expend muscular energy but at least they could tuck their legs underneath them rather more and run, if only for a short time. This was of great benefit to both predator and prey alike and any further adaptation along the same line would offer great potential for increased speed and increased size.

There was a problem however. As the thigh-bone moved increasingly into a vertical plane, it would have tended to have come up against the plates that made up the hip, in particular, the pubis, the bone that extended forward to hold the muscles that pulled the femur forward. Charig calls this 'the femur-knocking-against-the-pubis' problem. He suggested that it was solved by the dinosaurs in three ways:

- the large sauropods which all retained the saurischian pelvis did not need to change very much. The larger they grew the less they needed to adapt their pelves because their weight limited their length of stride.

- by going on to two feet. The effect of doing this on a permanent basis (as opposed to the occasional bipedality adopted by many lizards today) meant that the whole hip structure was tilted backwards and the whole pubis was set far enough away from the femur to allow for an increase in the stride.

- by eradicating the pubis altogether in the leading part of the hip structure. The muscles that formerly attached to it, began to attach instead to the ilium and the pubis itself 'migrated' backwards until it lay parallel with the ischium. It could well have been this arrangement that allowed the first tiny bird-hipped dinosaurs to evolve because they could take the long bounding strides that are typical of flightless birds today. It was only later that the pubis acquired a second forward pointing prong, though Charig cannot suggest an explanation as to why this happened.

One interesting consequence of this theory is that the major evolutionary step was a vertical limb posture. The two-footed gait – which for many scientists has been taken as a basic definition of the dinosaurian status – could emerge only after the creatures had learned to walk with vertical limbs. 'Only *after* an animal had reached the vertical stage,' concluded Charig, 'could it become a habitual biped.'

Seeley's distinction has stuck. From the 1880s on it was apparent that there was no real justification – in strictly zoological terms – for talking about 'dinosaurs.' The term has little more significance, scientists argue, than a number of other popular labels attached to groups of animals. It was, for instance, once common to lump together elephants, rhinoceroses and hippopotamuses as 'pachyderms' – thick-skinned creatures. But to group these creatures together was to elevate a secondary characteristic to the level of a primary one. Many animals may develop thick skins quite independently, indeed any large animal is likely to have a thick skin. The relationship between those three creatures is, literally, only skin deep. An analysis of their skeletons – the characteristics of which took far longer to evolve – reveal different relationships. Elephants belong in a group of their own; rhinoceroses are more closely related to horses; and hippopotamuses are close cousins to pigs. Again no zoologist would accept 'game' as a logical term of classification. There is after all no necessary evolutionary connection between creatures that are hunted. Bats are not birds and whales are not fish.

Yet the term persists. Paleontologists themselves – let alone the general public – go on talking about dinosaurs. If this book was entitled *The Day of the Saurischians and the Ornithischians* it would not have much impact and it seems likely that after a century of loose usage, the term will go on being used loosely.

The great division between the two dinosaur types was well established by the beginning of the Late Triassic, some 205 million years ago. For millennia, the single great continent of Pangaea had become steadily warmer. The climate was now set fair for over 100 million years. It would take that length of time for Pangaea to break up into the constituent parts that make the world today, and thus drastically modify the climate – a change that was, in part, to end the reign of the dinosaurs. On land the forests were dominated by giant relatives of small modern plants known as club mosses and horsetails, some of which grew to 100-foot trees, known as scale trees, because of their rough bark. Ferns and tree-ferns abounded in a form little different from those of today. There were a number of ginkgos, of which just one species remains today, a 'living fossil' that has been around so long that it seems impervious to disease, insects and even pollution. (Rediscovered in China in the eighteenth century. It was given the name of 'duck-foot tree' on account of the shape of its small six-part leaves and proved an ideal tree for urban planners in America.) Conifers too had spread rapidly.

Besides the dinosaurs, there were other Triassic land dwellers: many types of lizard, the small mammals and the remaining amphibians and a few other reptiles. These inhabited three major environments: the uplands – the result of early collisions of the continental land masses, now being worn away; the sweeping plains of the lowlands, which combined forest, marsh, desert and open savannah country; and the shores of the Tethys Ocean that divided the two super continents into which Pangaea had broken.

In the uplands, little was fossilized, except in the most odd circumstances. These occurred in the limestone hills of England's Mendip Hills in Somerset, and South Wales, where cracks and caves developed into which flood waters carried the remains of a few creatures. One of these was an odd-looking lizard which must be one of the first ever flying creatures, *Kuehneosaurus*. It was not a dinosaur but rather similar to the flying lizards of Borneo today in that it had ribs that extended sideways from its rib-cage to support a membrane with which it would parachute through the air – a sort of reptilian hang-glider.

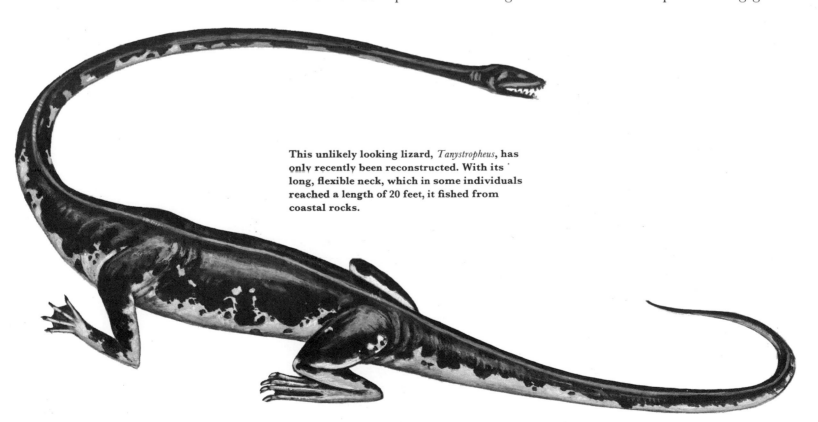

This unlikely looking lizard, *Tanystropheus*, has only recently been reconstructed. With its long, flexible neck, which in some individuals reached a length of 20 feet, it fished from coastal rocks.

Hips that Divide two Dinosaurian Orders

If dinosaurs had been discovered later and in greater abundance, the term 'dinosaur' – or indeed any term implying that they were all closely related creatures – would probably not have been proposed. For the group consists of two separate orders – saurischians or 'lizard-hips,' with pelvises resembling those of modern crocodiles; and ornithischians or 'bird-hips,' with a pelvic structure like that of birds (though there is no known relationship between ornithischians and birds).

In saurischians, the pubis thrusts downwards and forwards; in ornithischians, the pubis extends backwards parallel to the ischium or both backwards and forwards, as illustrated by the diagrams at right.

For simplicity's sake the drawings show only one side of the hip bones. As the front-on photograph of an *Iguanodon* skeleton shows, each half attached to the back-bone and provided support for each thigh-bone.

The reason for the evolution of the two hip types has been much in dispute. One persuasive theory focuses on the first small dinosaurs and their increasingly fast and upright mode of locomotion. With lengthening stride, the thigh-bone would tend to come increasingly close to the pubis. To solve this problem some dinosaurs – the ornithischians – evolved a new type of pelvis in which the pubis was swung round out of the way of the thigh-bone (in later versions the pubis reacquired a forward prong). Other types – the saurischians – opted for greater bulk and therefore avoided the need to take long strides. They gained safety in size rather than in speed.

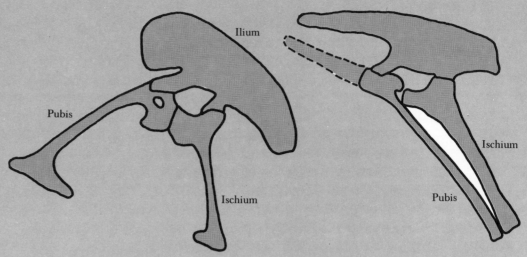

SAURISCHIAN PELVIS

ORNITHISCHIAN PELVIS, EARLY AND LATE (DOTTED)

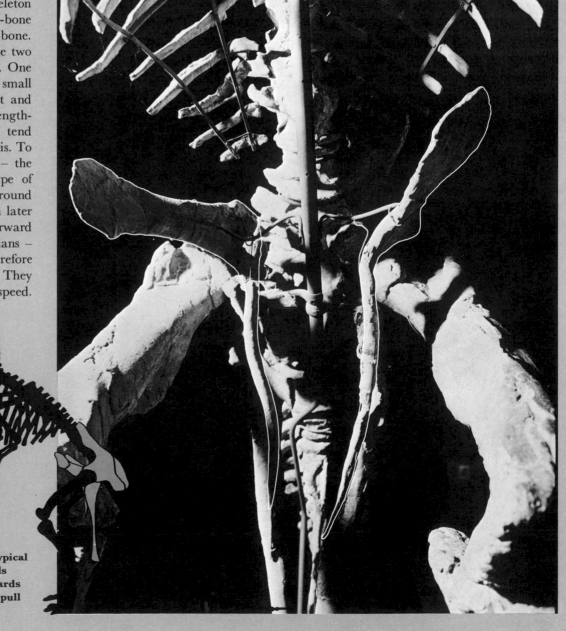

An *Iguanodon* pelvis shows the structure typical of later ornithischians. The pubis extends downwards in a thin rod as well as upwards and forwards to receive the muscle that pull the huge leg forward in walking.

On the shores of the Tethys Ocean – or at least those parts represented by caves and cracks of the Isle of Gliny, Poland – dwelled one of the most amazing creatures yet found, *Tanystropheus*. This was a lizard that ranged from a few feet up to several yards in length, half of which was neck. The proportions of the neck are quite startling. Some small ones have necks eight inches long yet only one inch wide. There is some fossil evidence that some of these creatures grew up to 40 feet long. It seems that this extraordinary snake-like neck was a sort of built-in fishing rod. Without leaving the shore, *Tanystropheus* could go fishing by plunging its head yards out to sea. From the same caves has come evidence of the first flying reptile known (see Chapter 5).

The lowlands were dominated by the dinosaurs themselves, who were to evolve steadily over the two successive periods, the Jurassic and Cretaceous. Although the Jurassic – named after the European Jura Mountains – was a time of stable and warm climate, many families of reptiles became extinct and others evolved over the 60 or so million years of this period. A number of marine reptiles, primitive land reptiles and gliding lizards vanished, while around the world the dinosaurs, in particular the lizard-hipped types, became dominant.

Much of the ground-work for modern knowledge about Jurassic dinosaurs had been done by Marsh in his excavations at Como Bluff. But that proved to be just an opening chapter of a continuing saga. The next major discoveries emerged at the turn of the century. The great dinosaur rush of the old West was a remarkable phenomenon, equivalent to a great gold rush in its way, even if only a few dozen people were involved. The rush coincided with the

Fabrosaurus, **a three-foot biped, is known only from a few jaw fragments but it is thought to be one of the earliest ornithischians.**

formation of the great institutions – Carnegie's Museum in Pittsburg, the Natural History Museum in Philadelphia, the United States National Museum, (a division of the Smithsonian Institution) in Washington, and, in particular, the American Museum of Natural History in New York.

The original museum, founded just after the Civil War, was housed in the south-east corner of Central Park but it moved shortly afterwards to its present site on Central Park West. Its development in the late nineteenth century was due largely to one outstanding paleontologist and administrator, Henry Fairfield Osborn. Osborn's career began as a sort of a joke. One summer day in 1876 he and a friend, William Berryman Scott, were chatting after having had a swim in a canal near Princeton. Scott had read one of Marsh's articles and jestingly suggested that they should go fossil hunting.

As jokes sometimes do, the suggestion took root and the following year,

In 1898 fossil hunters from the American Museum of Natural History came upon this fossil littered ridge near Medicine Bow, Wyoming. So abundant were the bones that a local sheep farmer had used them as building blocks to construct a cabin: hence the site's name – Bone Cabin Quarry. It proved a treasure house of Cretaceous dinosaur fossils.

accompanied by a raggle-taggle of other students, the two made their way west by rail. Before they left, they went to see Cope and, after he had overcome his first suspicions, he gave them every encouragement – the start of a relationship that developed into a lifelong friendship. Naturally enough, Cope's protegés hated Marsh. Once when Osborn and Scott went to Yale, Marsh had all the best fossils hidden away and then tracked them round the museum in carpet slippers, keeping a beady eye on them from behind storage cases to make sure that they did not stray from the official paths.

Scott spent the rest of his life at Princeton and in 1891 Osborn joined the American Museum of Natural History, where he founded the Department

Allosaurus (or *Antrodemus*) **was the most formidable of the Jurassic carnivores. Thirty feet long and weighing some two tons, it had ferocious talons on all four limbs for tearing at its prey. Striding along on its bird-like hind feet (right), it must have been the terror of** **Jurassic forests, filling the niche of a lion or tiger today. Its massive skull, designed to tear and gobble large chunks of flesh, was built to combine lightness and strength – as the skeleton (below) at Princeton's Museum of Natural History shows.**

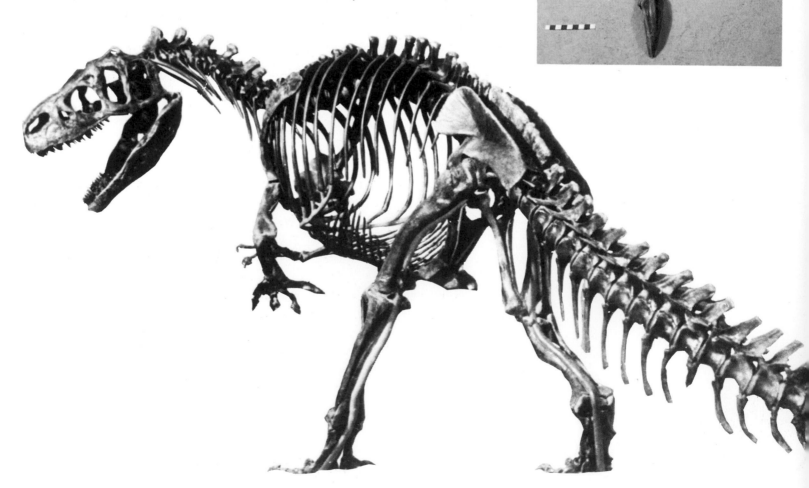

of Vertebrate Paleontology. At the same time he joined the Faculty of Columbia University in New York at which he founded the department of zoology and the graduate school. He became President of the Museum in 1908, a post that he held for 25 years.

One of Osborn's first major projects was to make a new exploration of the Jurassic Morrison Beds at Como Bluff. He was after both fossil mammals and dinosaurs (the second because he had an astute sense of what would attract the public to his burgeoning museum). The expedition was not at first a startling success, for Marsh had done a thorough job. In 1898 the party moved north to a ridge near Medicine Bow. There they found a hillside strewn with large fragments of dinosaur bones that had weathered out of the hillside. There were so many that a sheep farmer in the area had astutely used them as struts and beams in a cabin he had built for himself; hence the name for the quarry that was dug on the site – Bone Cabin Quarry. For six years the museum's scientists worked at Como Bluff, Bone Cabin and other nearby quarries and sent back their finds in freight cars supplied by the multi-millionaire banker, J P Morgan. In those six years the museum shipped back some 75 tons of bones, enough to occupy an army of paleontologists for decades. This, in conjunction with the finds made by Earl Douglass for Andrew Carnegie, provided a pretty good picture of the creatures that evolved during Jurassic times.

Of the lizard-hipped types, the small, delicate, fast-moving carnivorous Coelurosaurs were well established. During the Jurassic, a descendant of one of the Coelurosaurs, evolved into the smallest dinosaur yet known, *Compsognathus*. This little creature, which was hardly more than two feet long, holds a particularly important place in evolutionary theory because its skeleton is extraordinarily similar in shape and size to that of the first bird, *Archaeopteryx*. It was in fact even more like a naked bird than its predecessor, *Coelophysis*. As we shall see, it is possible that these tiny, delicate creatures, which would have lost heat very easily, grew feathers to insulate themselves and then adapted them for flight.

A larger contemporary of *Compsognathus*, living in Wyoming, was *Ornithol-estes* ('bird-robber'). These slender seven-foot creatures – of which several species are known – had long, slim, strong clawed fingers, suitable perhaps for the capture of an active and elusive prey. It has been portrayed making a grab at an early bird but could just as easily have seized small lizards and mammals. (These dinosaurs, though slender, could reach a considerable size. In the 1920s a 19-foot version, *Elaphrosaurus*, was found in the Tendaguru district of Tanzania).

The Jurassic also saw the evolution of the first of the giant flesh-eaters, the best known of which is our old friend *Megalosaurus*, the first dinosaur ever named. This is now one of the best represented types of dinosaur in Europe – there have been well over 100 separate finds in Europe alone and other similar types have been found in Australia, Greenland, India and the USA. The megalosaurs and their related species (of which there are probably several, though the finds have not been analyzed carefully enough to name them) must therefore have been some of the most successful animals of all time. They were solid creatures, varying from ten to 25 feet in length. The megalosaurian head was about one foot long and the teeth were shaped like miniature steak knives, serrated and often laid back into the mouth like sharks' teeth so that anything gripped in the jaws would have had little chance of escape. Its short, stout neck and its powerful back legs must have enabled it, like a shark, to grab great gobbets of flesh in its mouth and tear them off with shakes of its head and body.

There were other versions of this basic patent. One of them was the even larger *Allosaurus* (also known as *Antrodemus* because two separate finds, separately named, were later discovered to be similar) which grew over 40 feet long and had three-toed feet, in shape like those of a bird but ending in formidable clawed talons with which it could have torn apart its prey to get at the entrails in a matter of seconds. The creature weighed two tons and its footprints show that it had a six-foot stride.

Like most of the large flesh-eaters, *Allosaurus* had to combine lightness of skull with strength. Its muscles were needed to tear their prey and the less weight they had to carry in their skulls the better. Like many later dinosaurs, therefore, they had quite thin skulls which were full of fenestrations. But despite the size of the skull, the brain was no larger than that of a kitten. In addition, like all of the bipedal dinosaurs, the long powerful tail was used both as a balance and as a weapon to lash out at rivals for a kill. The bones at the back of the skull were loosely joined, snake-like, to allow for a wide range of movement when the creature swallowed large chunks of flesh. *Allosaurus* may or may not have been a hunter but it certainly fed on the carcasses of the giant plant-eaters that developed during the Jurassic. The American Museum has a skeleton of a plant-eater whose tail vertebrae are marked by the teeth of an *Allosaurus*. Some *Allosaurus* teeth were even found beside the sauropod skeleton – the teeth of these predators presumably replaced themselves continuously throughout their lives.

The other major evolutionary line of the lizard-hipped types led to the great plant-eaters, the sauropods, which are the dinosaurs everyone knows – vast creatures like *Diplodocus*, *Apatosaurus* (which used to be called *Brontosaurus*) and the largest of them all, *Brachiosaurus*. There were many types of these colossi but they all had the same ground plan – massive bodies, long necks, long tails, tiny heads and pillar-like legs. They ranged from one to over 80 tons. In 1972 remains of what might prove to be an even bigger sauropod dinosaur were unearthed in Colorado: one vertebra is five feet long, 60 times the size of a human's. If the structure of the whole beast was in proportion to the *Brachiosaurus*, it would have been 50 feet tall, 100 feet long and weighed up to 100 tons – roughly the size of the blue whale, the largest animal so far known to have existed. Together, therefore, these beasts hold the records for the tallest, longest and heaviest land creatures the world has ever seen.

As a result of the copies of the $87\frac{1}{2}$-foot find made available through the Carnegie Museum, the *Diplodocus* is perhaps the best known of all the dinosaurs. In fact it was quite a light creature in comparison to its length. It weighed not much more than ten tons, for it was mostly neck (22 feet) and tail ($50\frac{1}{2}$ feet). Over the years, countless people have gazed in awe at Carnegie's *Diplodocus* in the various manifestations of its 300 bones reproduced in plaster round the world. Thousands of children have paced out the tail, which peters away into tiny vertebrae, no wider than those of a little finger. It must have dragged along the ground as its owner plodded forward. The neck, like the head of a crane, was kept suspended in the air without any muscular effort by great cables of tendons attached to the shoulders; the tendons ran from

This *Brachiosaurus* skeleton was unearthed at Tendaguru and now stands in the East Berlin Natural History Museum. It was the heaviest (80–100 tons) and the tallest (40 foot) of all land animals. It owes its great height in part to the fact that its front legs are, uniquely, longer than its back legs.

The Start of a Popular Myth

The discovery that many dinosaurs had expansions – 'second brains,' as they were tabbed – of their spinal cords, inspired a journalist, Bert L Taylor on the staff of the *Chicago Tribune*, to pen a piece of doggerel. Often reprinted, the lines have done much to propagate a misunderstanding: the spinal enlargements – initially believed to have been necessary for dinosaurs to control the outer reaches of their bodies – were probably to accommodate glands.

> Behold the mighty dinosaur,
> Famous in prehistoric lore,
> Not only for his power and strength
> But for his intellectual length.
> You will observe by these remains
> The creature had two sets of brains –
> One in his head (the usual place),
> The other at his spinal base.
> Thus he could reason *a priori*
> As well as *a posteriori*.
> No problem bothered him a bit
> He made both head and tail of it.
> If something slipped his forward mind
> 'Twas rescued by the one behind.
> And if in error he was caught
> He had a saving afterthought.
> Thus he could think without congestion
> Upon both sides of every question.
> Oh, gaze upon this model beast,
> Defunct ten million years at least.

The last couplet points to two other misconceptions. There were many hundreds of 'beasts'; and dinosaurs have been defunct not ten million but 65 million years, at least.

A Dinosaur Pedigree

This diagram sets out the major dinosaurian groups and their presumed relationships, together with their distant relatives, the pterosaurs, birds and crocodiles which stemmed from the same thecodontian ancestors (far left).

The width of the 'branches' indicates the significance of families at any one time. The great sauropods for instance, declined at the end of the Jurassic and declined again during the Cretaceous. During the Cretaceous, the ornithopods underwent a dramatic expansion, producing a number

of new families and sub-families, some of which were still evolving new species at the very end of the age of reptiles.

The groups listed here offer no more than a rough indication of the wealth of dinosaur species that made up each group. Within the hadrosaur family alone, for instance, paleontologists recognize some 60 species.

The relationships suggested here reflect one of many theories about the relationship of dinosaurian families.

Often an attempted classification lends

a spurious rationality to the mass of diverse fossil material with which paleontologists constantly wrestle. The term prosauropod, for instance, suggests that the members of that infra-order were ancestral to the sauropods, yet this is now dismissed by many scientists.

The origin of the birds remains a mystery. They have been derived from both orders of dinosaurs by different scientists – and even from crocodilians – but they could also have stemmed from some thecodontian ancestor.

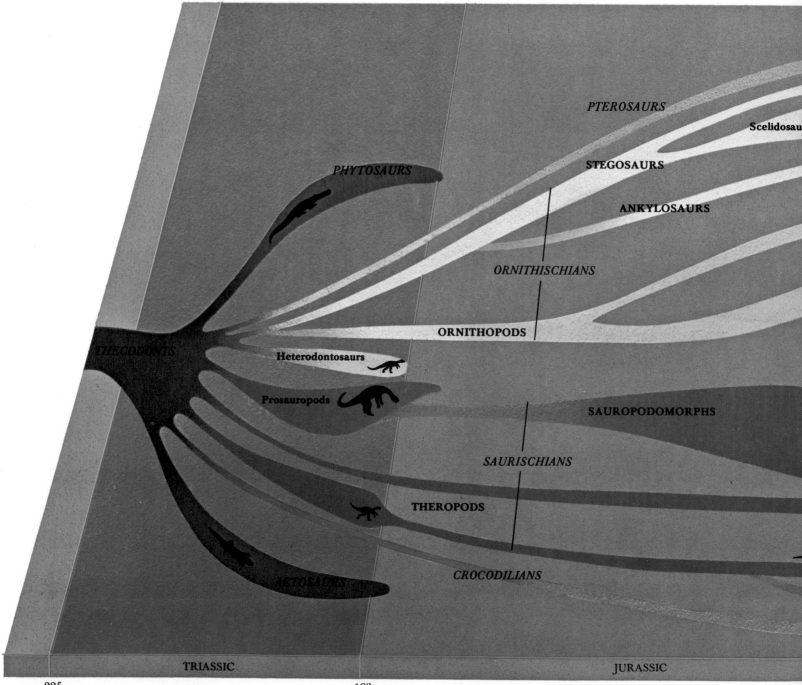

THIS CLASSIFICATION is one of several currently considered acceptable. Each family or subfamily – here given the formal Latin names – contains many species, the number of which is indicated in brackets. They amount to some 550, but this is an approximate guide only, for many species are defined on the basis of just a few fossil finds; there are others suggested on evidence too scanty for general acceptance; and, finally, known species represent only a fraction of those that actually lived.

ORDER ORNITHISCHIA
SUBORDER ORNITHOPODA
  Family Pisanosauridae (1)
  Family Heterodontosauridae (4)
  Family Hypsilophodontidae (11)
  Family Iguanodontidae (32)
  Family Hadrosauridae
    Subfamily Hadrosaurinae (40)
    Subfamily Saurolophinae (6)
    Subfamily Cheneosaurinae (5)
    Subfamily Lambeosaurinae (15)
  Family Psittacosauridae (6)
  Family Pachycephalosauridae (9)
SUBORDER STEGOSAURIA
  Family Stegosauridae
    Subfamily Scelidosaurinae (4)
    Subfamily Stegosaurinae (21)

SUBORDER ANKYLOSAURIA
  Family Acanthopolididae (11)
  Family Nodosauridae (29)
SUBORDER CERATOPSIA
  Family Protoceratopsidae (5)
  Family Ceratopsidae (46)

ORDER SAURISCHIA
SUBORDER THEROPODA
Infraorder Coelurosauria
  Family Procompsognathidae (4)
  Family Podokesauridae (9)
  Family Segisauridae (1)
  Family Coeluridae (28)
  Family Ornithomimidae (17)
Infraorder Carnosauria
  Family Ornithosuchidae (12)
  Family Popsauridae (1)
  Family Megalosauridae (53)
  Family Spinosauridae (2)
  Family Tyrannosauridae (21)

SUBORDER SAUROPODOMORPHA
Infraorder Prosauropoda
  Family Anchisauridae (32)
  Family Plateosauridae (21)
  Family Melanorosauridae (9)
Infraorder Sauropoda
  Family Camarasauridae
    Subfamily Cetiosaurinae (15)
    Subfamily Brachiosaurinae (23)
    Subfamily Euhelopodinae (7)
    Subfamily Camarasaurinae (7)
  Family Atlantosauridae
    Subfamily Titanosaurinae (28)
    Subfamily Atlantosaurinae (10)
    Subfamily Diplodocinae (9)
    Subfamily Dicraeosaurinae (2)

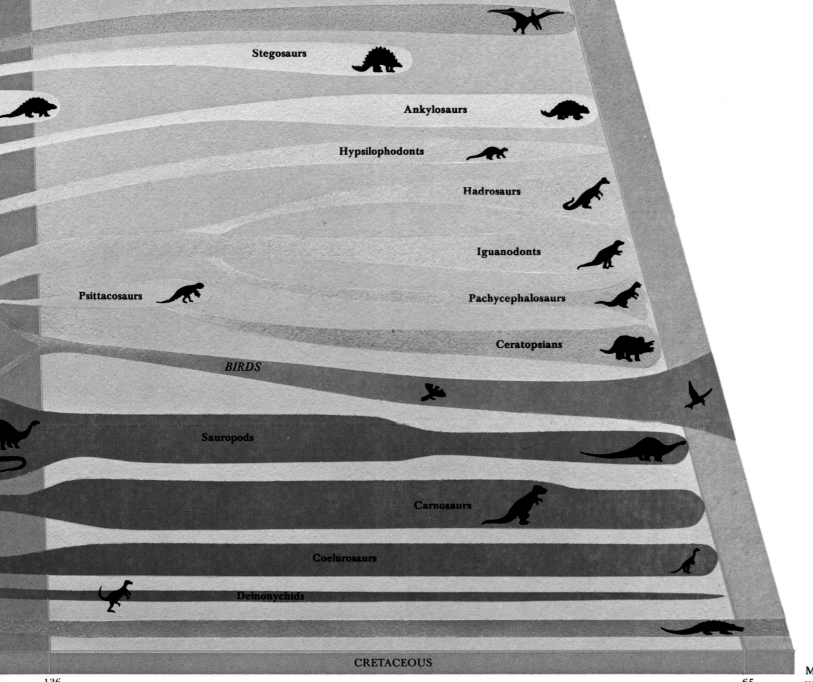

Stegosaurs

Ankylosaurs

Hypsilophodonts

Hadrosaurs

Iguanodonts

Psittacosaurs

Pachycephalosaurs

Ceratopsians

BIRDS

Sauropods

Carnosaurs

Coelurosaurs

Deinonychids

CRETACEOUS

Millions of years ago

powerful muscles up the neck vertebrae and inserted into the top of the head.

Diplodocus and the others of his kind were truly marvelous creations. From the engineering point of view, the problems of being a giant are considerable. Whales survive happily enough in the water because they are supported by their own environment. If stranded on a beach, however, they rapidly suffocate under their own weight: a whale's skeleton is not strong enough to support it, and its lungs are crushed. *Diplodocus* solved that problem: it is built like a bridge. The back is arched and the legs are pillar-like supports that plunge straight down, with flexion at the joints.

The front legs of all but one of the sauropods – the *Brachiosaurus* – were shorter than the hind legs, a possible evolutionary reminder that they could have been descendants of the two-footed meat-eaters and that their four-footed stance was a response to their growing weight. Their legs were very like those of elephants, with short, heavy toe-bones and an extended pad behind and beneath the bones of the foot to take up the shock of impact. Calculations have shown that the legs of the *Diplodocus* have a safety factor of four – that is, it could have supported its whole weight on one leg, or even born the weight of three other *Diplodoci* on its back. (In the case of the *Brachiosaurus*, this is an astounding thought, for an 80-ton *Brachiosaurus* must have been able to support a burden of a couple of hundred tons if correctly loaded).

It used to be commonly assumed that these huge creatures spent most of their life in water to avoid the necessity of having to support their giant weight on land. Buckland even called the first sauropod discovered *Cetiosaurus* or 'whale lizard'. If elephants are the largest terrestrial mammals known today, it was thought, how could the giant dinosaurs have grown so much larger unless they were supported by water? Consequently many reconstructions of the sauropods show them standing in 20 or 30 feet of water with just their heads appearing above the surface. In this position, it was thought, it would have been able to breathe well enough, for the nasal openings in most species were high up on the head; and in this manner, too, it could have escaped the carnivorous bipeds that patrolled the shore-lines. Finally the sauropods typically had weak rake-like teeth that could have been used for hauling up masses of soft, dense, tropical water vegetation.

Additional evidence about the sauropods' way of life comes from trackways. In November 1938 a Mr Roland Bird, then collecting for the American Museum of Natural History, was drawn to Glen Rose, Texas, about 40 miles south and west of Fort Worth, after discovering that a block of masonry containing the tracks of a carnivorous dinosaur had been built into the wall of a local courthouse. Such finds were common in the area. Along the bed of the nearby Paluxy River, Bird discovered some odd looking pot-holes. They appeared not to have been made in the normal way, by stones swept around in the current. The holes, partially filled in with mud and sand, lay in shallow water. Bird, suspecting the nature of his discovery, cleared one of the prints out with a spade and broom. With delight, Bird saw that he had found the three-foot footprint of a great sauropod dinosaur. Bird set about organizing help. Fortunately for him, Roosevelt's New Deal was well established, with its variety of government sponsored programs to drag the US out of depression. One of these schemes was the Works Progress Administration, established in 1935 'to help men keep their chins up and their hands in.' Backed by the museum and the University of Texas, Bird whipped together a team of WPA employees. In 1940 his crew built a dike to divert the Paluxy, dried out the river bed and set to work excavating. The huge prints were exposed. Moreover it appeared that the sauropod had been followed by a carnivorous

Exposing bones at the Monument

One of the great names in the annals of American dinosaur hunting is Earl Douglass, who in 1909 found a complete *Brontosaurus* skeleton. Born in Minnesota in 1862, Douglass went to the University of South Dakota, taught in Montana and in 1902 joined the staff of the Carnegie Museum in Pittsburg.

In 1908, while in the field in Utah, he discovered a *Diplodocus* femur weathering out of rock near the Green River, near the

dinosaur whose three-toed, bird-like tracks were equally visible, sometimes overlapping the prints of its intended prey. There were no marks of a tail dragging on the ground behind the giant footprints. It seemed reasonable to assume that the sauropod had splashed along in the shallow water that came up to its knees, hotly pursued by a predator. How did the chase end? No one knows. Both trails vanish, tantalizingly, before the conclusion.

Later Bird found another trail in Banderia County, Texas, which offered proof that the sauropods liked deeper water as well. The tracks are those of the front feet only, lightly impressed in the mud. The animal, almost floating, must have moved by walking along the bottom with its front legs. There is one mark, and only one, of a hind leg, apparently indicating that the beast had changed direction with a smart kick downwards. As a result of these discoveries, the sauropods were relegated either to the shallows, or to deep water.

But there were some puzzling things about the sauropod skeletons. Surprisingly they were built for lightness. The skeleton of a sauropod typically weighs about half that of a whale skeleton of the same size. As Henry Fairfield Osborn at the American Museum of Natural History noted, lightness of skeleton is a walking, or running, or flying adaptation and not at all a swimming one.' Perhaps, he suggested, the sauropods emerged from water occasionally to breed and while on shore they could have used their great height to browse on treetops. Besides, the evidence of Bird's trackway at Glen Rose was contradictory. The tracks of the left and right legs were separated by a mere three or four feet – an indication that the limbs were set for efficient, economical locomotion pointing immediately down from the hip

Douglass and the Dinosaur Monument

point where it emerges from the Uinta Mountains on its course towards the Grand Canyon. The next year he returned to identify the stratum (the fossil-rich Morrison Formation of Cretaceous age). Throughout the spring and early summer, he and a white-bearded Mormon, George Goodrich, scrabbled along the outcrops of the formation, searching for fossils.

On August 17, Douglass spotted the glint of fossil bone and after scratching, digging and probing around it for a while, he found that it was a vertebra of a very large dinosaur. Moreover, it was attached to other vertebrae. By evening, he had identified his find as eight tail bones of a *Brontosaurus* (soon renamed *Apatosaurus*).

Douglass was exhilarated, and urged a large scale operation, with the backing of Andrew Carnegie. Planning for a long campaign, he recruited men and farm equipment from nearby ranches, and bought tools for digging and carting the heavy sandstone and soft shales. His wife and one-year-old child arrived to spend the winter with him. That first year they lived

hard in two tents, heated by an iron stove, using a sheep herder's wagon both as an office and as a dormitory for three assistants.

From now on, the *Brontosaurus* became Douglass's career. He did not want to settle in the nearby town of Vernal because it would take too long to ride to work. He homesteaded some spring-fed land, built himself a log house, laid out fields, bought a cow and some chickens, and planned a self-sufficient existence. There he was to remain for ten years.

The task before him and his workers was gigantic in every sense. The skeleton was contained in a stratum that had been tipped up on its side. The giant fossil was also set facing *into* the rock. To get at the skeleton, the men had to burrow downwards and inwards on either side. To do this, the team used dynamite, manpower, horses and a mine railway to cart away the debris. The rails were laid and relaid along the bottom of the trench as it sank deeper and deeper into the ground.

Finally, the trench was 600 feet long and 80 feet deep and on its steeply slanting wall

were exposed enormous numbers of dinosaur bones, predominantly of *Brontosaurus*, *Diplodocus* (*D. carnegei* was named for Douglass's sponsor) and *Stegosaurus*.

Douglass had, apparently, found a dinosaur graveyard, probably formed by a sand-bar in a large river on to which carcasses had been washed and then covered with sediment. The necks and tails of the large sauropods were sometimes spread out as if they had been washed continuously by the action of the stream.

There was one major problem: Utah was being settled. At any moment, a prospector might happen along and file a claim for the dinosaur lands. In 1915, a solution was found. President Woodrow Wilson set aside 80 acres around the quarry site and named it the Dinosaur National Monument, an area which has now been enlarged many times. By 1923, the museum had 300 tons of dinosaur bones and skeletons. With the death of Andrew Carnegie, the museum pulled out, leaving further work to be done by the United States Government, through the United States National Museum.

and tucked well in under the body, and therefore designed to carry a heavy weight easily.

The idea of deep-water sauropods was finally dispelled by findings from a completely different branch of science. Research by physiologists in Vienna in the first two decades of this century showed that humans could not breathe through a tube in water that was more than three or four feet deep. At that depth, the water pressure on the lungs becomes too great and the chest muscles simply cannot operate. Divers can only breathe because their air-supplies are under enough pressure to counteract that of the water. Even whales cannot breathe in unless they are lying flat on the surface; the explosive hiss that accompanies the release of air from a whale's lungs is the result of the pressure of the water even at the depth of their own bodies. In the 1950s, these finds were applied to dinosaurs by Kenneth Kermack of University College, London. A *Diplodocus* standing at a depth of 30 feet would be subjected to pressure on its body of about double that of ordinary atmospheric pressure; to overcome such pressure, the muscles of the respiratory system would have needed to generate tremendous power – so much that they would have weighed several tons. There are no bones that would have acted as a framework for such muscles.

To get an idea of the problems facing our hypothetical *Diplodocus* standing in 30 feet of water, breathe out, hold your nose, shut your mouth, and try to expand your lungs by breathing in. You are now attempting to create a vacuum in your lungs, which a *Diplodocus* would have to do to draw air down its long neck. It simply cannot be done. Even if a *Diplodocus could* have managed it, the air would only be at half the pressure of the surrounding water. The poor creature would have to fight continually to retain anything in its lungs at all.

In 1971 the various lines of evidence were effectively pulled together by Robert Bakker, a vertebrate paleontologist at Yale (now at Johns Hopkins, Baltimore), whose thinking on dinosaurs has done much to popularize and revolutionize the subject. In a brief, tautly argued paper entitled 'Ecology of the Brontosaurs,' published in the most eminent of scientific journals, *Nature*, Bakker argued that brontosaurs (by which he means sauropods as a whole)

For such a mountain of flesh and bone, the brachiosaur's head (right) seems strangely small. It is hard to see how it could have consumed a sufficient quantity of food to supply its needs. Some scientists have suggested a solution based on the fact that the creature's nostrils were set in the top of its head. Such an adaptation is usually associated with water dwellers. Perhaps, runs the theory, it wallowed in the shallows eating water plants. Possibly – but its massively heavy lower limbs also equipped it for life on land where it could have browsed on tree tops inaccessible to its more diminutive cousins.

were *not* water creatures by nature. They were more likely to have been plains-dwellers, only venturing into the water rarely. His arguments are:

- high-placed nostrils are no argument for living in water. There are many lizards – like iguanas and monitors – which have large external nostrils, high on the snout. These are used for smelling and for filtering air, not as snorkels. Besides, he suggests, brontosaurs might have had a trunk, which would be reason enough for having nostrils set high up on the top of the head;
- aquatic animals tend to have long flattened tails to help with swimming but sauropods have whiplash tails which would simply have dangled uselessly in the water;
- sauropod teeth may be peg-like but they are well adapted for grinding up coarse food and often show too much wear to be associated with soft, watery plants. Besides they might have had gizzard stones or gastroliths, to help with their digestion, as some crocodilians do today. Some skeletons, indeed, have been found with concentrated masses of small stones among the ribs;
- aquatic quadrupeds are normally round-bodied. Land-dwellers – like elephants – have deep thoraxes. The brontosaur rib cage was more elephant-like than hippo-like;
- the brontosaur's vertebral column was superbly adapted to support its weight. It had short vertebrae, with tall spines on the top of them to provide effective muscle attachments;
- if the brontosaur did not need to support itself on land, it would not have such strong straight, elephantine legs. Of large animals today, those that do not need to support their weight for long can flex their elbows and knees. 'Brontosaur limbs were very straight, columnar

This cetiosaur thigh-bone, found near Oxford in the nineteenth century and now in the Oxford Museum, gives a dramatic indication of the scale of sauropod dinosaurs. The bone was flattened during fossilization, a process that produces this 300 pound monument of rock.

A little girl sits amazed in a sauropod footprint in the American Natural History Museum. Sauropod feet were padded pillars over three feet across, similar in shape to those of elephants.

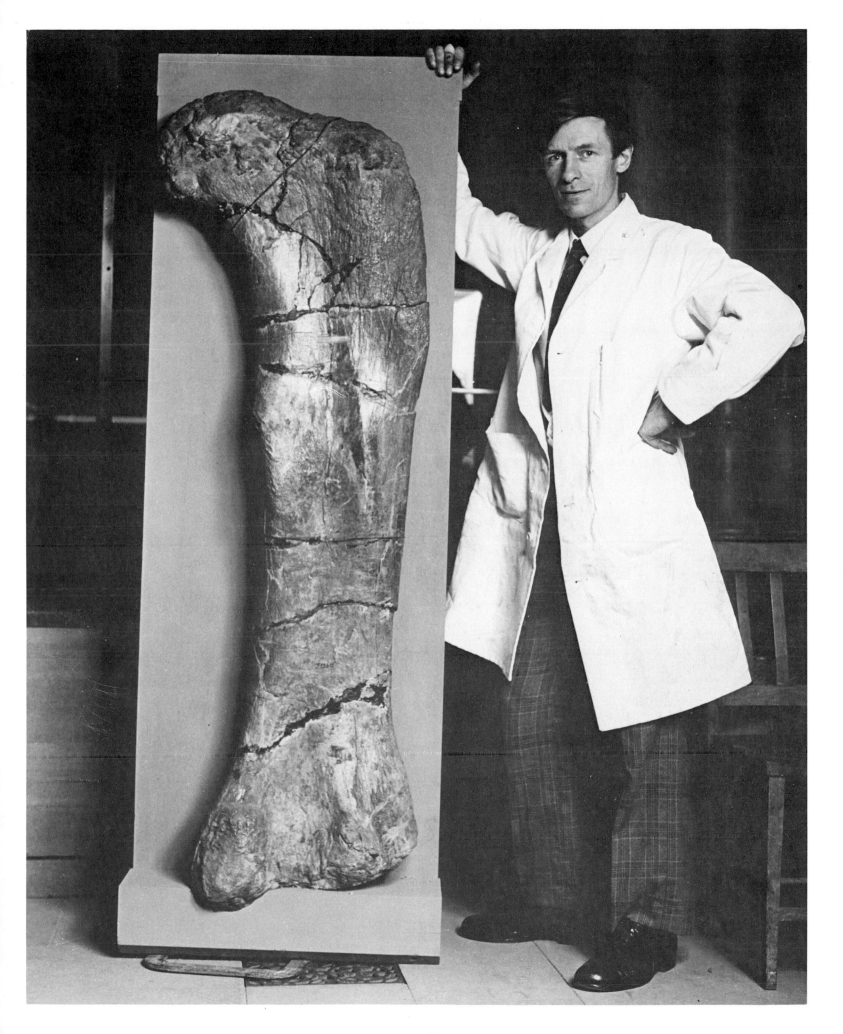

A herd of *Diplodoci* make their way slowly across a North American Jurassic landscape towards distant water. In the background, two rear up on their

hind legs to reach succulent leaves – behavior that, though probably rare, was quite within their physical capabilities.

and elephantine,' Bakker points out, 'the combination of elephant-like limbs and powerfully braced backbone argues strongly for terrestrial habits for brontosaurs.'

– aquatic animals tend to have widely spread toes to stop themselves sinking in, yet the brontosaur's toes were very compact, like an elephant's. They could not have ventured into marshy ground for fear of bogging down and starving to death.

– tall creatures are, without exception, browsers on terrestrial plants – elephants, giraffes, okapis, camels. Brontosaurs, Bakker argues, had a long reach because, they, too, were land-based browsers.

– seaside and lakeside environments are limited, yet the sauropods show remarkable diversity. Such diversity corresponds to a diversity of niches only available for land-dwellers.

– finally it has been argued that sauropods fled to the water for safety. In fact Jurassic and Cretaceous meat-eaters seem as well adapted to the water as the plant-eaters, and the water would therefore have offered no great defense. Anyway traveling in herds, as elephants do, would have offered a surer defense, especially in conjunction with the ability to use the tail as a whiplash.

The giant plant-eater *Diplodocus* – at almost 90-feet the longest land creature ever – weighed a scant 10 tons. Its neck and back vertebrae were hollowed out for lightness.

The image that emerges from Bakker's analysis is that of a herd trampling through lowlands, browsing on the foliage of trees that were too tall for other herbivores to reach. Sauropods, in fact, must have combined the advantages of super-elephants and super-giraffes. And such behavior would have been ecologically necessary: these herds of plant-eating creatures could have demolished acres of foliage at a single meal, opening up a forest area – rather as a forest fire and elephants do nowadays – allowing the smaller shrubs, plants, trees and grasses to flourish and thus renewing the cycle of growth.

All in all Bakker's arguments conjure up a remarkable vision of efficient, if huge, animals plodding – and occasionally jogging – in herds from forest to forest, protecting their young, well able to cope with their 80-ton bulk. Brontosaur, remember, means 'thunder-lizard'; they were not perhaps very lizard-like but their progress must on occasion have certainly been thunderous.

All the creatures discussed so far were of the 'lizard-hipped' type. The Jurassic also saw the development of the first bird-hipped dinosaurs – those that were to evolve in later ages into the upright herbivores like *Iguanodon* and a wide variety of armored dinosaurs. This type had emerged first in

Fabrosaurus in Triassic times. The line had not proved particularly dramatic but it had endured and now emerged in one of the most intriguing of the smaller dinosaurs, *Hypsilophodon*, which means 'high-crested tooth.' This neat and nimble creature, four or five feet long, was a fast mover. In some ways it was a primitive in that it retained a five-fingered hand and a foot with four very long toes. Like other bird-hipped species later it possessed the tendons that kept the tail rigid as a stabilizer sticking out behind it.

Hypsilophodon was first described in 1882 and because it seemed to have such good fingers and toes, it was first thought to have been a tree-climbing reptile that ate fruit and leaves. It is now well known from 20 or so skeletons, all of which have been found in the Isle of Wight. It was recently discovered that its back feet could not grip branches, though it nevertheless might have climbed

Hypsilophodon **used to be portrayed as a tree dweller because it had prehensile toes but this 'primitive' ornithischian – in fact one of the most successful of dinosaur species – had long, slender lower limbs that mark it as a fast runner. In addition – as with all ornithischian dinosaurs – its tail was stiffened with bony tendons to balance it when running.**

into trees as a defense against predators, or to feed, as goats do (goats surely remain one of the most unlikely animals to find in a tree, yet they are extremely good at climbing). However it lived, it was certainly extremely effective and remained unchanged almost until the extinction of the dinosaurs themselves.

The first of the large, bipedal, bird-hipped plant-eaters was *Camptosaurus* ('bent reptile') a 15-foot, three-ton creature. Its size marked it out as a new development in dinosaurian physique. It was like a primitive *Iguanodon*; it had curved thigh-bones (hence its name) – as opposed to the *Iguanodon's* straight ones – and probably therefore tended to go down on four legs a good deal. It had a long, flat head, with ridged and closely packed teeth that were adapted for crushing plants. It also had a bony beak-like ridge instead of a lower lip. The floor of its lower jaw was grooved, perhaps to take a long tongue that could whip out, seize plants, then retract to allow the plants to be sliced off by the hard beak before the food was chopped up by the teeth. It also had elastic cheeks – an adaptation possessed now only by mammals – which allowed it to take much larger mouthfuls and chew its food over and over again before swallowing it. This made for efficient digestion.

During the Jurassic there also evolved the first of the heavily protected dinosaurs. Various defenses had already been adopted – size, aggressiveness, herding, fleetness of foot – and there now emerged a new range of adaptations which evolved as 'hands off' protection against the giant carnivores. The way was shown by *Scelidosaurus*, a four-legged relative of *Fabrosaurus*. *Scelidosaurus* has two claims to fame. Along its 12-foot body it had small triangular spikes, a hint of the heavy armor that was to enclose its descendants. It also lacked in its bird-hip the forward prong that defined the hips of its descendants.

The teeth of *Scelidosaurus* – close-set, cylindrical, with a flower-shaped crown – offer a clue to its way of life. Its remains were found in marine sediments, and it was first thought that the animal would have been equally happy munching up sea-side vegetation, or swimming out to look for marine prey. Now, however, it seems more likely that it was purely vegetarian and that it lived on soft plants by rivers and lagoons.

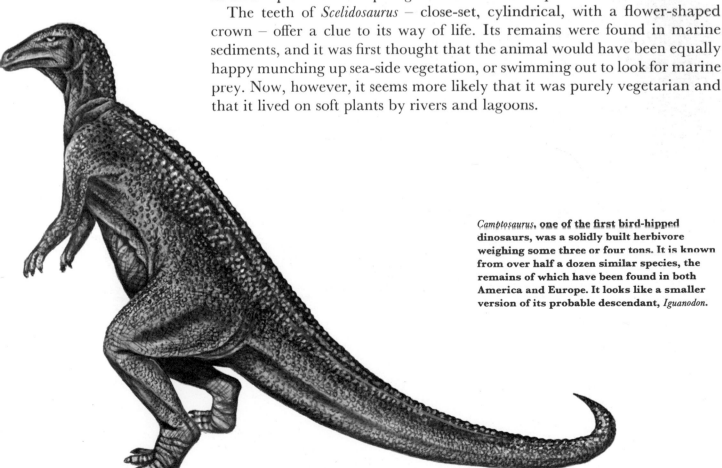

Camptosaurus, **one of the first bird-hipped dinosaurs, was a solidly built herbivore weighing some three or four tons. It is known from over half a dozen similar species, the remains of which have been found in both America and Europe. It looks like a smaller version of its probable descendant,** *Iguanodon.*

Kentrosaurus **was an East African stegosaur and a contemporary of** *Brachiosaurus*. **Its spikes were less formidable than they look. They were not part of the skeleton but attached to the skin.**

After *Scelidosaurus* emerged two of the oddest looking lines of dinosaurs: the spikiest, *Kentrosaurus*, and perhaps the strangest of all, *Stegosaurus*.

Kentrosaurus was a quadruped with an extraordinary protective range of spikes down its backbone. The spikes ran in pairs, with an extra pair sticking out of its hips. Those that ran down its tail must have made formidable weapons.

In *Stegosaurus*, which is found chiefly in North America, these spikes have evolved into huge plates, making the creature into one of the most popular of all the dinosaurs. Stegosaurus, a bulky plant-eater, weighing nearly two tons, is well known from a number of skeletons. It was first described by Marsh in 1877 who wrote in wonder: '*Stegosaurus* is one of the strangest of animals.' It is still something of a puzzle. The creature had ridiculously short front legs and yet it was permanently quadrupedal. In its hind leg, the thigh bone is remarkably long, about the size of an elephant's femur and about twice the size of its lower leg bones which makes it look as if its knees were much too low for comfort. It also had a tiny skull.

Its most remarkable features were the great plates that flowed down its back – triangular, bony excrescences that towards the rear turned into spikes, of which the tail possessed two pairs. Marsh restored it with the plates sticking up in the air in pairs, a restoration that has been the source both of its appeal and of considerable controversy. One difficulty with Marsh's view was that no plates had been found in pairs; another was that no one could think of a very good purpose for the plates. If they were supposed to be a defense, it would have been easy enough for a predator to move up alongside the creature and tear away at its flanks. Besides they were set into the skin, not the skeleton and could not have been all that rigid. Later a skeleton was found with the plates fossilized not in pairs but alternately and some restorations go along with this view. Perhaps, however, the alternation of the plates reflected the conditions of fossilization, not the creature's actual appearance. Many scientists now tend to think that the plates were set flat, flopping over sideways to cover the flanks. Even so they could hardly have been very effective for their size. Perhaps they helped radiate heat; but why should the stegosaurs, of which there were many different species, need radiators when other larger dinosaurs did not? Or perhaps they were some form of bizarre sexual characteristic, a dinosaurian version of the weird and colorful plumes that define the many species of the birds of paradise in present-day New Guinea.

The beast was an oddity in other ways as well. Its head was not much bigger than that of an Alsatian dog and its brain was the size of a walnut. Whatever the qualities of many of the dinosaurs – a question that we will return to in the next chapter – it is difficult to think of the stegosaur as a particularly bright creature.

When the stegosaur was first discovered, it was noticed that there were enlargements to the spinal cord in the pelvic region. Such enlargements were a common feature of many dinosaurs but in *Stegosaurus* the cavity was 20 times

Although known from only a few specimens found in Folkestone and Cambridge, England, *Acanthopolis* was apparently a primitive version of the armored dinosaurs. Its thick, bony plates evolved in later species into heavy armor and imposing knobs and spikes.

As yet it is not certain how the plates of *Stegosaurus* – one of the most popular of all dinosaurs – would have looked in real life. They are usually restored sticking up in a great frill (left), but in this position they would have offered little defense. They could perhaps have extended sideways (above) to protect the creature's flanks, but even so they do not look very effective. It could be that they acted as radiators to dissipate heat or that the animal could raise and lower its plates to frighten off would be predators.

the size of the brain proper. It was at first assumed that the dinosaur needed the enlargement as a local nerve center – or second brain – to control the movements of the great back legs. This was such a captivating image that it inspired a piece of doggerel so popular that its concepts wormed their way into the general interpretation of dinosaurs (see p.84). In fact the enlargement of the area through which the spinal column ran was probably a gland which may have stored glycogen, or animal starch, a chemical used in muscular reactions, and could thus have been a store of ready energy for emergencies. The ostrich has a similar glycogen gland in the same part of its body today – a possible reminder of its far distant relationship to the dinosaurs.

Stegosaurs were a wide-spread group of dinosaurs. Remains of them have been found in Africa, Europe and North America. But they became extinct, shortly after the end of the Jurassic; why, no one knows. It may have been something to do with the changes that marked the beginning of the Cretaceous. The seas began to rise and eventually divided the already diverging continents into two continental islands. If the stegosaur's plates really were an adaptation to heat, it is possible that the increasing humidity that must have accompanied the end of the first great age of dinosaurs simply exterminated the niches to which the stegosaurs were adapted and, along with their habitats, went the stegosaurs themselves.

The Great Fossil Safari of Tendaguru

Tendaguru is one of the great names in the history of dinosaur hunting. For from Tendaguru – about 40 miles inland on the southern boundary of Tanzania – came the largest of all the known dinosaurs, the 80-ton *Brachiosaurus*, and, in addition, bones of scores of other species in overwhelming abundance.

Sixty years ago Tendaguru was an inaccessible spot, four days' march inland from Lindi, a seaport of the then colony of German East Africa. In 1907, an employee of the Lindi Prospecting Company found several gigantic fossil bones weathering out of the ground at Tendaguru. By chance, a German expert on fossil reptiles. Eberhart Farrs, was in the colony at the time and came to see the bones. He found a veritable dinosaurs' graveyard – an immense collection of fossil bones scattered through the tall grass beneath the scrubby trees and gleaming in the sunlight. Back in Germany, Dr Farr's reports sparked passionate scientific interest. The Berlin Museum raised some 200,000 marks – the equivalent in purchasing power of perhaps half a million dollars – and despatched a team to the area.

There, techniques had to be worked out from scratch. No fossil hunters had worked before in the tropics. The Germans coped by establishing a huge operation. Pit after pit was excavated by up to 500 native laborers, many of whom brought their families along. The excavations became a sort of huge village, a commune of anything up to 1000 men, women and children. There were no roads and no trucks. Everything – food, scientific gear, fossils – had to be carried on the heads and backs of porters.

The leader of the expedition, Werner Janensch, trained a local overseer, Boheti bin Amrani, who rapidly showed himself to be a brilliant fossil hunter. The results were magnificent. During the first three years of work, 4300 loads of bones were packed off down to the coast. In four years, Janensch shipped out 250 tons of bones.

The most dramatic find, of course, was *Brachiosaurus*, now mounted in the Berlin Museum, its head rearing some 40 feet above the floor. But there were many other finds, in particular a number of plated dinosaurs like *Kentrosaurus*.

It seems probably that in the late Jurassic, about 140 million years ago, the Tendaguru dinosaurs had lived along the mouth of a river, for the area displays an alternation of fresh water sediments, which contain the bones of giant dinosaurs, and marine sediments containing seashells. The river may have had a great bar across it that prevented the mixing of marine and fresh water. A later excavator at the site, an Englishman, John Parkinson, described the scene as follows: 'A long lagoon separated from the open water by a firm-edged bank of sand was there, with a big river . . . probably terminating in a delta, opening by various mouths, shifting, silting up and changing behind its sandbanks, as does the Niger. At the entrance to the lagoon, pebbles and the larger grains of rock would settle downwards, but the rotting carcases, buoyed up by the gases of decomposition, floated onwards to slow dismemberment.'

The British continued the work after the First World War, when Tanganyika was created from the former German colony. The area is by no means exhausted of fossils even yet.

JANENSCH AND HIS TEAM WITH SAUROPOD LIMB BONE

A sauropod skeleton lies exposed.

Africans work a Tendaguru open-cast quarry, its face protected from wind and rain by a wall of branches.

Fossil finds neatly packed, Janensch's porters set off from Tendaguru to the coast.

Lifelike models of a mother and baby *Triceratops* – one of the most successful of later dinosaur species – stand by a waterhole in Hamburg Zoo.

4/The Golden Age

The Cretaceous was a period of great change, for during this time, from about 136 to 65 million years ago, the great super-continent of Pangaea finally broke up. In the north, North America split away from the European land mass; in the south, Antartica, Australia, South America and Africa all drifted apart; finally Africa and Europe divided to create a primitive Mediterranean. These events were to prove momentous. For the first time for many hundreds of millions of years, the earth's life forms were cut off from one another, isolated on huge continental islands. During the Triassic and Jurassic periods, the dinosaurs had been much the same the world over. By the late Cretaceous, they were very different.

In the south, which divided a little later, there was little change. The great Jurassic sauropod and carnivore species lived on – if in reduced numbers – to the end of the Cretaceous. But in the north more intense evolutionary pressures favored the bird-hipped types. The great sauropods and their carnivorous predators went into a decline and herbivores evolved new and weird types – tank-like ankylosaurs with clubbed tails, dinosaurs with horns and frills, duck-billed dinosaurs. Environmental changes – most significantly, perhaps, the spread of the flowering plants, which were established by the mid-Cretaceous – must have provided more evolutionary niches to be filled. But such diversity proved of no avail: not a single dinosaur survived beyond the end of the Cretaceous.

The natural world in the Cretaceous would have seemed much more familiar to us than the Jurassic. Gingko trees and conifers, already ancient species, were common. But newly evolved pines, firs, oaks, ash, poplars, sycamores and willows also dotted the landscape. In the undergrowth, magnolia bushes and viburnum thrived; holly had appeared for the first time;

there were climbing plants like roses, grape-vines and passion-flowers; banks of saxifrage provided patches of cover, along with euphorbias and heather. Many of the landscapes would have been splashed with the colors and scents that we know today. The new range of plants provided new niches for small creatures. Bees and other insects evolved their peculiar relationship with the flowers, feeding on them and pollinating them. And – perhaps the most telling change of all for a time traveler – there were birds: the gull-like (but toothed) *Hesperornis*, the speedy tern-like *Ichthyornis* and species that resembled cormorants, divers, herons, rails and moorhens.

Other groups of animals too, evolved into forms familiar today. Snakes appeared (although not apparently poisonous ones). The lizards diversified. The mammals slowly extended their range from the shrew-like creatures of the Early Jurassic to varied (if still small) creatures that resembled possums and hedgehogs. There even appeared, late in the Cretaceous, a tree-shrew, an aggressive solitary little creature that has survived little changed ever since. This was the remotest ancestor of the primates, the line that includes the monkeys and apes and, of course, finally man himself.

Much of what is known of the Cretaceous was the result of the last of the North American dinosaur rushes, which began in about 1910 in western Canada, particularly along the Red Deer River in Alberta. A number of discoveries had been made before in Alberta. Prospectors had identified rich fossil beds along the Red Deer River and also pioneered a new prospecting technique from rafts that acted as a base, a viewing station and a ferry for scientists and their finds. There were two main groups involved, one headed by Barnum Brown of the American Museum of Natural History, the other by Charles Sternberg who worked with his three sons, George, Charles and Levi, for a number of institutions, in particular the National Museum of Canada, the Royal Ontario Museum and the Canadian Geological Survey.

Barnum Brown was raised in his parent's pioneer cabin in Kansas, where his father was a farmer and a coal merchant. Brown got his degree at the University of Kansas where he met Marsh's former assistant, Sam Williston. He took part in a number of fossil hunting expeditions and then, in 1897 was hired by the American Museum of Natural History, thus beginning an association that lasted until his death in 1963. The hall devoted to Cretaceous dinosaurs in the museum is virtually a monument to his collecting skills.

In 1909 a rancher from the valley of the Red Deer River on a visit to New York spotted the similarity between the fossils on display there and bones he had found on his own ranch. Brown was so impressed with the rancher's story that he set off for the town of Red Deer the next year. He decided to build a barge large enough to hold his camp and all his fossils. When finished, the barge was 130 feet long by 12 feet wide, and in the middle of it there was a large tent, complete with stove and chimney. The journey down river was a great success. By the end of the summer, the flat-boat was piled high with fossils, all carefully encased in their plaster jackets. Brown returned again the following year. By collecting from beds at different levels, he was able to compare the evolution of species in one small area.

His successes galvanized into action the Geological Survey of Canada who did not like to see their fossil treasures being carted off by Yankee bone-hunters. In 1912 they called in the Sternbergs who equipped themselves with a wagon and a row boat, and began to explore Drumheller, 100 miles downriver from Red Deer. They had a good first year, unearthing a good haul of duck-billed dinosaurs.

The following year, both teams were back again, working an area between

Steveville and Dead Lodge Canyon. This time, the Sternbergs had a flat-boat of their own with a motor boat to pull it. Fortunately there were more than enough fossils for all; in this one area, some 100 dinosaurian skulls and skeletons were collected, including some of the finest late Cretaceous dinosaurs ever found – several duck-billed forms, armored dinosaurs, the carnivorous dinosaur *Gorgosaurus*, and the spiky *Styracosaurus*.

Brown continued his work through 1914–15 and the Sternbergs remained until 1917. In 1916 after another good season, Sternberg, accompanied only by his youngest son, Levi, shipped off a couple of duck-billed dinosaurs to Britain, aboard a steamer, the *Mount Temple*. Unfortunately the *Mount Temple* was torpedoed and the dinosaurs vanished into the Atlantic. But the following year the loss was redeemed somewhat by the discovery of a superb *Gorgosaurus*, that was eventually named as a separate species after Sternberg.

The year 1917 brought the end of the great Canadian dinosaur rush and also the end of an era. Roads and automobiles had ended the day of the lone fossil hunter camping out and scanning the ground for likely spots. The Cretaceous beds between Steveville and Dead Lodge Canyon are now a park with a number of shelters containing exposed fossil skeletons. Visitors rely on their imagination to recall the days of the Sternbergs and Barnum Brown.

As a result of these and other finds, scientists now have a good general idea of the evolution of dinosaurs during the Cretaceous. Of the lizard-hipped types, the sauropods continued much as they always had done, evolving new species that were in many respects the same as the old ones. How they were related and how they should be classified is a matter of such debate that most of the experts in the field have made their own suggestions. It is worth reviewing these suggestions to show how tangled matters can get scientifically.

Normally the sauropods are divided now into two families but their names have changed many times over the decades, as paleontologists argue over the significance of the number of sacral vertebrae and the exact angle of the hip-bones. The problems can be illustrated by taking as a starting point the name *Brontosaurus*. *Brontosaurus* was first used as a general term for a giant sauropod. It was also applied to one particular genus. Other similar finds were also called *Brontosaurus* (as a general term) but the names and relationships of these finds on the genus level were soon a hopeless muddle. In 1887 Marsh named one of his sauropod families the Atlantosauridae, which contained three genera, *Atlantosaurus*, *Apatosaurus* and *Brontosaurus*. In 1956 the famous vertebrate paleontologist, A S Romer, said that all these three, plus a fourth, *Titanosaurus*, were synonymous with Marsh's *Apatosaurus*. Ten years later, he decided that *Atlantosaurus* and *Brontosaurus* were the same and *Apatosaurus* was different. Another expert, writing more recently, has decided that *Atlantosaurus* is different and that *Apatosaurus* and *Brontosaurus* are the same. And so it goes on. As things stand at present, there is officially no such creature as a *Brontosaurus*. It is called *Apatosaurus*, which is fine for the experts who tell each other what they are talking about by writing '*Apatosaurus* (= *Brontosaurus*)'; but they still talk vaguely of the 'brontosaur,' meaning a sauropod (which is why Bakker entitled his 1971 *Nature* paper 'Ecology of the Brontosaurs.' It is confusing to say the least for members of the public who have known of the *Brontosaurus* as a popular favorite for years and will no doubt go on talking about it for years to come.

So forget about terminology for the moment, and take the general point: the giant sauropods continued, though in smaller numbers (for reasons suggested in the final chapter), right until the end of the Cretaceous. Upon

Though its ferocity is in dispute, *T. rex* in this restoration glares down from its 17-foot height as befits the world's largest land carnivore.

A life size tyrannosaur tooth reveals minute steak-knife serrations along the cutting edge.

them – or their carcasses – fed the two-footed, lizzard-hipped predators which now evolved into the most ferocious carnivorous creatures of all time. The biggest of all, and the one known to every child over the age of about three, was *Tyrannosaurus rex* – 'the King of the tyrant Reptiles.' (This creature, by the way, is the only dinosaur that is popularly known by its full species name, rather than by its single generic name.)

T. rex was certainly a most amazing creature. It was first found in sediments known as the Hell Creek Formation of eastern Montana by Barnum Brown. He found two superb *T. rex* skeletons, one of which is in New York and the other in the Carnegie Museum in Pittsburg. The creature measured over 40 feet from snout to tail (though the last few feet of tail were missing) and it carried its head some 17 feet above the ground. This is a considerable height – three times that of a human being and almost on a level with the world pole-vault record. The ones Barnum Brown found must have weighed about eight tons but it is possible that really large tyrannosaurs weighed ten tons. It had a four-foot skull and teeth that ranged up to six inches long and an inch wide. They were serrated along their edges and curved inwards. Each of the teeth, of which there were several dozen, was thus like a small curved dagger, sharpened and serrated like steak knives on both sides. Its powerful back legs raised the beast's hip region ten feet off the ground; its knee would have been level with a human head. No wonder it has been the star of so many monster-movies, striding across the land spreading fear and destruction in its wake.

In fact its traditional image has now been slightly modified. It used to be portrayed towering in an upright pose, with a long tail which swung about or trailed on the ground. In fact its tail was relatively short and bulky and since it must have helped with the balance, it was probably held above the ground. Like others of its kind, it probably did not walk upright, but horizontally, its tail acting as a counter-balance to its body. With that great bulk to carry, it did not even run. Footprints of tyrannosaurs have been found and they show that it had a stride only about three feet long. It has also been suggested that it

These comparative models reveal *Tyrannosaurus rex's* bulk: a human being would scarcely have reached the creature's knee cap.

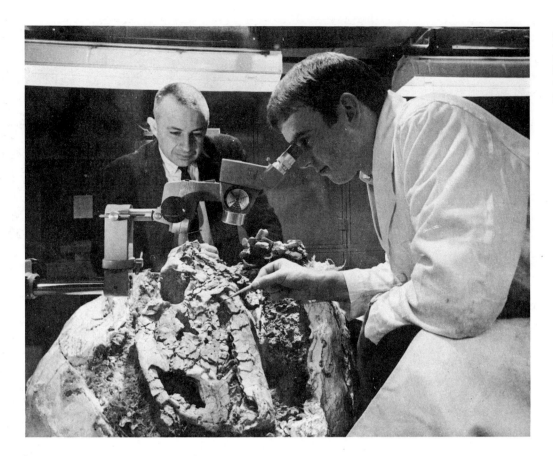

would not have been an active predator – it would not have pursued and killed its prey. Firstly it could not move fast enough; almost all dinosaurs would have been able to outrun it. Even a sauropod would have given it a good race. Secondly even if it had caught and attacked a victim, its teeth are for eating, not for killing; they would have snapped off in the battle and would not have been available to perform their first function of providing meat for the creature. The vicious claws that capped its toes would certainly have been capable of tearing open even the largest of the sauropods but to tackle a live and active one would have demanded a one-legged kick, a feat of balancing skill outside *T. rex's* repertoire. The claws may have been used to dismember corpses but were probably most useful to retain a good foothold. Those who cannot bear to see the king dethroned, should be reassured: the view that *T. rex* was a carrion eater and not a killer is by no means universally held. Many paleontologists still see the creature as a predator.

The really odd thing about the *T. rex* is the size of its forearms, which were not found with the original skeletons. When traces of them *were* found, to everyone's surprise they turned out to be only a couple of feet long, smaller than human arms. They certainly could not have been used to seize prey, or to help in the tearing up of food. In addition they seem to have been highly specialized: they have only two fingers, as opposed to the usual three, and

T. rex was restored (right), its forearms – tiny, but well muscled and with two pointed claws – posed a problem. They could not have been used in killing or eating. One theory suggests that they were used to establish balance on standing up (below): the claws may have acted as a break to prevent the animal sliding forward as it reared into an upright position.

A *Tyrannosaurus* finishes off a hadrosaur. Although the small herbivore could certainly have outrun the cumbersome predator and although it has been suggested

that *T. rex* was a carrion-eater rather than a killer, it would certainly have made short work of any young or injured dinosaur it could catch.

they were long and spindly. It was once suggested that they were used as toothpicks but the creature could not even reach his mouth with them. No one has yet devised and substantiated a satisfactory use for the delicate front claws. Perhaps the most persuasive suggestion comes from Barney Newman, of the British Museum (Natural History). It is possible, Newman writes, that the fore-limbs were used to shift the weight backwards, over the back legs as the beast got up from the prone position. The evidence for this lies in the fact that the tiny limb with its well developed claws was supported by a strong pectoral girdle, indicating that it was well supplied with muscles. *T. rex* might have rested by squatting down, chicken fashion, its legs tucked underneath it. If from this position it simply straightened its legs to get up, it might have overbalanced forward, or simply pushed its head along the ground, without ever getting upright. Conceivably the claws of the front legs locked into the ground, giving it a slight but necessary backwards purchase, allowing the creature to throw its head back and then straighten its legs.

The original *T. rex* was found in the USA but the other great northern land-mass was well supplied with very similar creatures. Indeed there is a whole family named after *Tyrannosaurus* which contains several genera. Russia is particularly well supplied with them, notably *Gorgosaurus* and *Tarbosaurus*.

The later carnosaurs were, however, not all massive. Some were small and almost certainly active predators. One, *Deinonychus*, is of particular importance. It was discovered by Dr John Ostrom of Yale in 1964 in Montana and it is one of the most exciting of post-war finds. It was a lightly built biped, nine foot long from head to tail. The tail was long and locked out behind it by a series of ossified rods. In life it probably carried its head four feet above the ground. *Deinonychus* means 'terrible claw' – an apt name, for it only walked on two of its three claws. The third was held several inches off the ground and was modified into a lethal five-inch, sickle-shaped talon. To use it, the creature must have been extremely agile; in addition to being a fast runner, it must have been able to stand on one leg and use its other leg, karate fashion, to slash at its would-be prey. Its arms, too, were long and equipped with claws, so that it could either grapple its prey to its chest or hold it at arms' length to disembowel it with a kick.

It is possible that *Deinonychus* represents a whole group of dinosaurs yet to be discovered, for in 1965 in the Gobi Desert of Mongolia, a pair of huge forearms were found, very like those of *Deinonychus*, except four times the size. The animal has been named *Deinocheirus* ('terrible hand') and if it really was a larger version of *Deinonychus* it would have been even more formidable than *Tyrannosaurus*. Imagine a 12-foot-high creature able to run at 30 or 40 mph, with sickle claws two foot long on its feet! But in fact such a creature would not probably have been able to move with corresponding speed and it is possible that the huge forearms belonged to a different sort of animal altogether – as yet unidentified.

Just as the carnosaurs increased in size, so did their fast moving relatives, the coelurosaurs. The small, bird-like coelurosaurs of earlier times evolved into large 'ostrich dinosaurs,' the best known of which are *Ornithomimus* ('bird mimic') and *Struthiomimus* ('ostrich mimic'). Both were indeed very like ostriches and probably filled a similar niche. They had long legs, compact bodies, long necks, hooked beaks and could undoubtedly run very fast. Of course they had fore-legs instead of wings, a reptilian tail and no feathers but they were probably omnivorous, as ostriches are, and could survive either by

The tracks of flesh-eating dinosaurs form some of the most common of dinosaurian relics. Those shown here are *Megalosaurus* tracks from the Isle of Wight (below) and Swanage (right), England. Such tracks can reveal the weight, stride-length and speed of the dinosaur concerned.

snatching up young dinosaurs, or picking fruit off trees with their long, agile fore-limbs. It is possible that they also stole dinosaur eggs. One bird-mimic in Mongolia was found intermingled with the eggs of a late horned dinosaur and was therefore named *Oviraptor* ('egg stealer'). Other coelurosaurs were undoubtedly predatory, as was shown in 1971 when a small agile *Velociraptor* ('swift robber') was found with its slender legs and long clenching hands grasping the skull of a small armored dinosaur. Apparently the struggle ended in the death of both creatures, who were then fossilized as they had fallen.

The most dramatic development in the Cretaceous was the extension in range of the bird-hipped dinosaurs, all herbivores. One successful type was the *Iguanodon* and its relatives in North America and Africa. One *Iguanodon* relative from the Sahara, first described in 1975, was found to have a sail-like fin down its back. Africa was then, as now, across the equator and a fin extensively supplied with blood vessels may have helped it to radiate excess heat and thus preserve its efficiency.

A second group of bird-hipped dinosaurs were the armored creatures of which *Stegosaurus* was the ancestor. Although stegosaurs became extinct in the early Cretaceous, their relatives the ankylosaurs proved extremely efficient. *Ankylosaurus* itself, from which the group is named, was armored with flat plates which were fused to its skin all over the top of its body. Weighing some three tons, *Ankylosaurus* must have scurried along under its tank-like armor plating almost immune from assault. It had stocky legs and a bony lump on the end of its tail which could have dealt a very nasty blow.

Among the most extraordinary of recent finds are the remains of so-called deinonychids. One, *Deinocheirus* or 'terrible hand,' was named after the formidable eight-foot forearms shown at left, which were found in Mongolia. The other, a mere three-foot high, was found in Montana (right). It is named *Deinonychus* ('terrible claw'), after the scimitar-like claws on its feet. Its tail was enclosed in stiff, bony rods to hold the tail rigid as an aid in balancing.

Other creatures in the same group developed variations on this theme, protecting themselves with spikes, plates and other knobbly excrescences. Ankylosaurs were found all over North America, Europe and Asia (though not as yet in Africa or Australia) and survived successfully right until the end of the Cretaceous.

A third group of bird-hipped dinosaurs were dome-headed. These, the pachycephalosaurs, the 'thick-headed reptiles,' had skulls several inches thick but were quite delicately built otherwise, with no natural defenses. They may have filled the niches taken nowadays by sheep, goats or ibexes. They are little represented in the fossil record and therefore, since fossils tend to occur most frequently in lowlands where sediments are laid down, the dome-heads possibly inhabited uplands away from the larger predators. That possibility at least suggests a reason for their thickened heads which were well rounded and would have been of little use in attack or defense. The skulls could have been the dinosaurian equivalent of ram's horns today. Males may have squared off to engage in ritual battle at mating time. Perhaps the mountainous regions of Asia and North America echoed in springtime to the clash of bone meeting bone as dome-headed males charged and butted each other into submission for possession of a herd of docile females.

Yet another group of bird-hipped dinosaurs were the hadrosaurs or duck-billed dinosaurs, named after their rounded upper jaw, which was flattened at the tip. The front edge of the bills were curved over into a sort of beak.

The Would-be King of Albania

NOPCSA IN CARICATURE

Frans Baron Nopcsa (pronounced 'Nopsha') von Felsö-Szilvas was, as his name suggests, one of the most outlandish students of dinosaurs. He was born into a noble Transylvanian family, in a remote corner of Hungary, and rapidly emerged as both brilliant and cosmopolitan. He wrote in four languages – Hungarian, German, French and English – on an impressive range of subjects: not only on dinosaurs, but also on geology, archaeology, ethnology and, in particular, on the then Turkish province of Albania.

Nopcsa, of whom no one had a higher opinion than he did himself, wrote his first paper on dinosaurs when he was a freshman at the University of Vienna. His paper described the skull of a new type of hadrosaur which his sister had found on the family estates. 'Is it not marvelous,' he later boasted to Dollo, the great expert on *Iguanodon* in Brussels, 'that I, so young a man, have written such an excellent memoir?'

With the collapse of the Turkish Empire in the early years of this century, the question of who should rule Albania was a much disputed international question. Nopcsa suggested himself as the ideal ruler. He offered to conquer the country for Austria-Hungary, proposing to dramatize his arrival by riding down the streets of Tirana on a white horse. He said he would marry the daughter of an American millionaire – he did not mind which – to support the economy. (He did not qualify for the job.)

During the First World War, Nopcsa served as a spy in the Austro-Hungarian army. Between sorties, he dashed off papers on dinosaurs and fossil reptiles.

He lost much of his wealth during the war and when peace came he was appointed President of the Hungarian Geological Survey. His aristocratic airs, however, and his rather delicate mental state – to cap everything, he was a homosexual – made it impossible for him to cooperate with his colleagues and he finally set off on a 3000 mile motorcycle trip around Europe with his secretary, a man named Bajazid, who was also his lover. They kept going until they were destitute.

In 1933, Nopcsa cracked. He spiked Bajazid's tea with a sleeping draught and then, while Bajazid was asleep, shot him. In a farewell note he explained: 'I did not want to leave him ill, miserable and poor, for further suffering in this world.' Nopcsa then shot himself through the heart.

This scene is a group portrait of some species common in Central Asia towards the end of the Age of Reptiles. At left is a *Tyrannosaurus* (better known from finds in North America). Two hadrosaurs, *Saurolophus*, look up at its approach. At right stands an ornately crested ceratopsian. In the foreground at right stand the ancestral – but enduringly successful – ceratopsians, *Protoceratops*; and at left in the foreground the parrot-faced ceratopsians, *Psittacosaurus*. In the background are two sauropods, survivors of a much-diminished family.

Clearly the hadrosaurs could have consumed a wide variety of plant life and were well suited to dealing with the tough flowering plants that had evolved by the late Cretaceous. In 1922 the stomach-contents of a mummified *Anatosaurus* ('duck-reptile') were found: not long before its death, the creature had had a meal of conifer needles, twigs, fruit and seeds. To cope with their diet, hadrosaurs' jaws were most unusual. They had batteries of teeth, so that their upper and lower palates ground together like millstones. A typical flat-headed hadrosaur, *Anatosaurus*, had anything up to 60 rows of teeth on each jaw, each containing six or more layers, one above the other, which would be used in succession as the outside layer wore away. An *Anatosaurus* had over 1000 teeth in its head. The food was continuously pressed back between the jaws by elastic cheek pouches.

Hadrosaurs are known from an extraordinary number of species, many of them very much alike. Hadrosaurian finds have been made in many European countries, in Russia, in the Far East, in North America and South America. So well represented are they in the fossil record that it is possible to build a hadrosaurian family tree. Many of the hadrosaurs had webbed hands and flattened tails, indicating that they spent some of their lives in water.

Scolosaurus was an ankylosaur, a group of heavily armored dinosaurs. This 18-foot, two-ton animal was armed with a mace-like tail and was covered with thick, bony plates which made it look like a giant, spiky tortoise.

The extraordinary domed skulls and the bony nodules of the pachycephalosaurs – or 'thick-headed' dinosaurs – have long puzzled scientists. The nodules that fringe the back of the skulls (right) may have been sexual attractants. The skulls, several inches thick, may have evolved for ritual head-to-head charges (below) to establish male dominance.

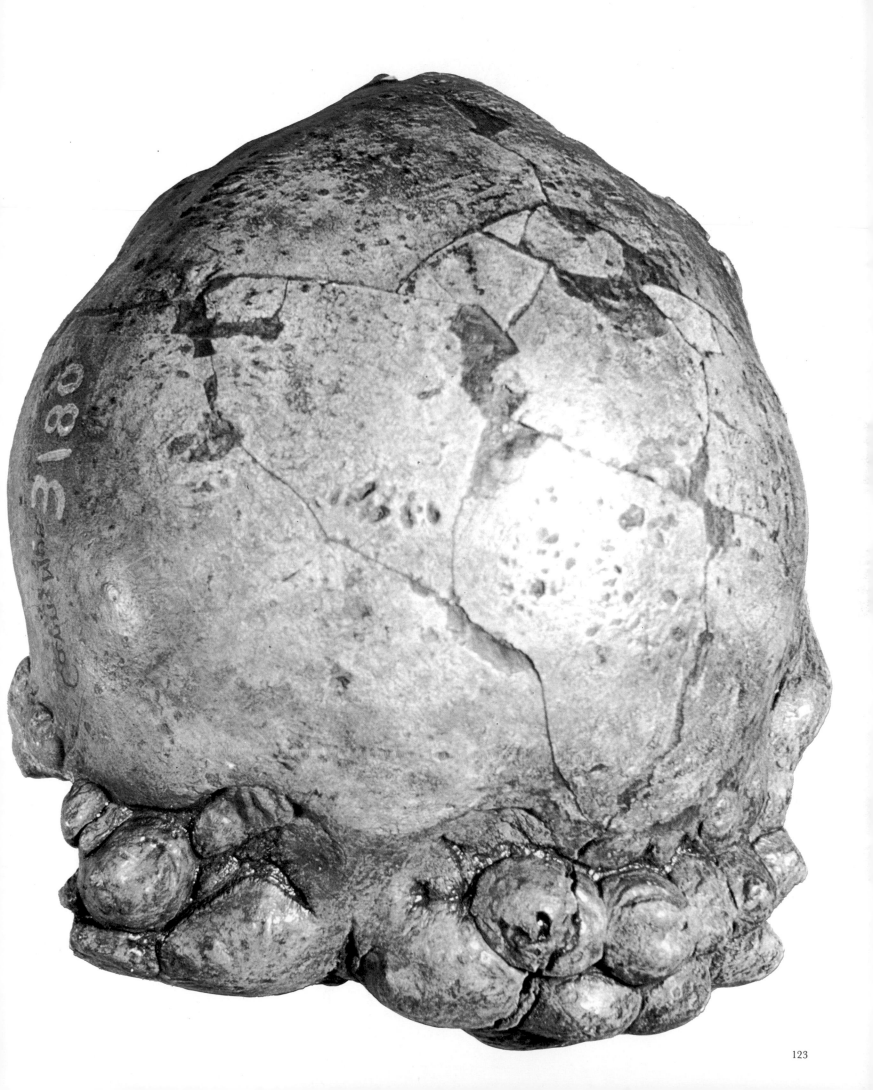

Many species were flat-headed, many others had crests, of which some were solid crested. Some of the solid crested hadrosaurs developed spikes that ran back from the brows and stuck out of the crown of the head; in others the spike ran forwards; and in the hollow crested species, many had dramatic crests that swept back 'like the plumes in a cavalier's hat.' The space inside the crest was connected with the nasal passages.

These sweeping hollow crests have been the subject of considerable speculation. Perhaps the oddest attempt at an explanation came from one of the oddest of paleontologists, Baron Nopcsa, a Hungarian, who was obsessed not only with dinosaurs but also with Albania of which he planned to make himself king (see box p.119). In 1929 Nopcsa stated his belief that there were not nearly as many species as there seemed to be; the crested ones were male, he said, and the flat-headed ones female. The great plume of *Parasaurolophus* was merely a sexual signaling device. Unfortunately since they are in fact separate species, many of Nopcsa's 'males' are found in different strata than the 'females,' and would have been separated by many tens of thousands of years, an insuperable barrier to breeding.

Other scientists suggested variously:
- that the extensive crests were snorkles to allow the animal to feed while submerged (though there were no openings on the top of the head);
- that they were air locks to prevent water leaking into the lungs while the creatures were swimming (although the water pressure would have far exceeded the air pressure inside the skulls and would have leaked in anyway);
- that the air sacs inside the skull were a kind of aqualung (although the space involved could only have been a few percent of the capacity of the lung itself);
- that the beaks and plumes together were supports for muscles of an elephant-like trunk (although there would be no conceivable benefit in having both a trunk and a duck-bill).

It seems most likely – according to John Ostrom at Yale – that the extended nasal passages were connected with the hadrosaurs' sense of smell. In the late Cretaceous landscapes, which contained so many new varieties of plants, any device that would help establish a new niche – by allowing a species to concentrate on the particular food source – would offer a new evolutionary advantage. Different species could then have co-existed without direct competition for food. This has occurred frequently in mammal communities, and the sensitivity of many mammalian noses is staggering. A rabbit, for instance, has 100 million olfactory cells. Mammals maximize the surface area available for smelling with bony convolutions and millions of delicate hairs. Reptiles seldom have such intricate senses; but hadrosaurs may have had: their crests and the air passages they contained could have vastly extended the skin surface available for analyzing smells. Since they lacked defensive weapons, a delicate sense of smell would also have allowed them to scent a potential predator in good time to flee.

If so they must have depended on their other senses as well. Perhaps they had color vision, to distinguish their food sources, their own kind, and possible predators. Almost certainly they had a good sense of hearing, for one hadrosaur skull has been found with the bone of the middle ear preserved. This bone, only 2.5 millimeters wide at its thickest, was so delicate that it must have been sensitive to very small vibrations.

Ostrom's arguments suggest a picture of hadrosaurs as living rather as

The Bobby and the Diplodocus

In a world of scientific professionals, amateurs can still make their mark. An example occurred in 1977. Two years previously, Stephen Hutt, a London policeman and a keen amateur fossil hunter, was digging into a cliff face on the Isle of Wight when he found some pieces of a bone embedded in rock. He dug the bits out and took them to the Natural History Museum in London. There, in 1977, they were tentatively identified as parts of the tail of a *Diplodocus*. Scientists were amazed.

Diplodocus, long known from the 87-foot skeleton assembled at the turn of the century, was thought to have been limited to North America. Yet here was evidence that the species may have lived in Europe as well. Moreover, *Diplodocus* was meant to have died out 140 million years ago, at about the end of the Jurassic, yet Hutt's find indicated an age of only 110 million years – well into Cretaceous times, when the families of all giant sauropods had been much reduced.

hoofed mammals do in southern Africa today – a huge variety of species co-existing in interlinking communities, some feeding on grasses, some on bushes, some on trees, vulnerable to predators but alert to the slightest danger, and skittishly ready to heave themselves off out of harm's way.

One hadrosaur find represents a particularly remarkable case. In 1908 the famous collector, Charles Sternberg, discovered in Wyoming a specimen of *Anatosaurus* in which all the parts that had been preserved were covered by mummified skin. It was not the skin itself, of course, but a representation of it in new chemical form. Possibly the animal had died naturally out in the sun and had then been dried out by the heat until the skin was hard and leathery. At this point, the creature's corpse may have been overwhelmed by a flash

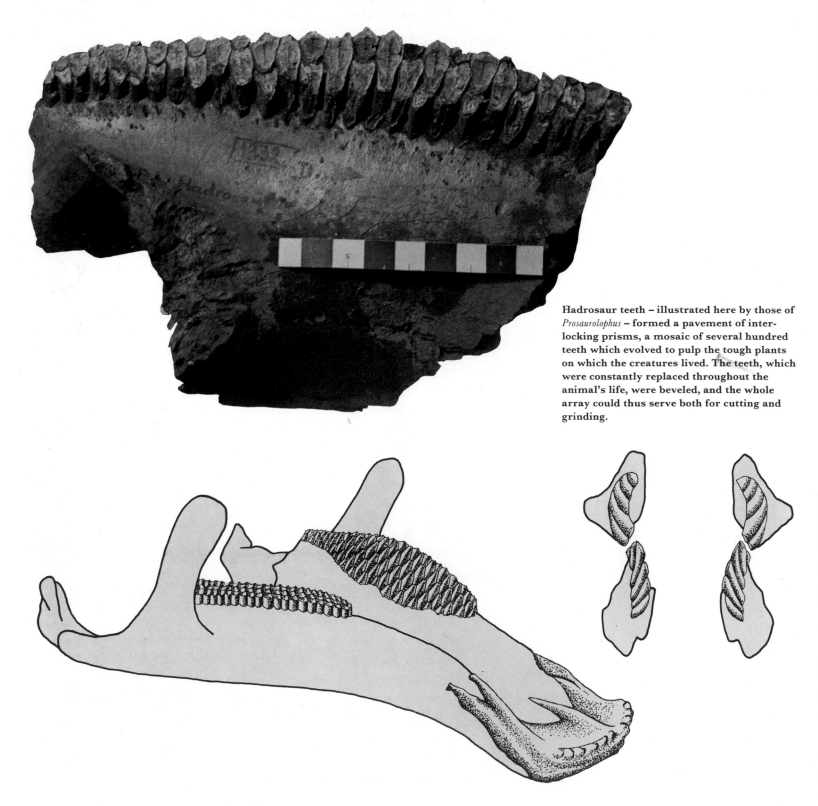

Hadrosaur teeth – illustrated here by those of *Prosaurolophus* – formed a pavement of interlocking prisms, a mosaic of several hundred teeth which evolved to pulp the tough plants on which the creatures lived. The teeth, which were constantly replaced throughout the animal's life, were beveled, and the whole array could thus serve both for cutting and grinding.

A Dinosaur in the Flesh

Perhaps the most fascinating item on the list of dinosaur relics is fossilized skin. The first such find appear in 1908, when the great fossil hunter, Charles Sternberg, was working in southern Wyoming with his three sons, Charles, George and Levi. They were running short of supplies. The elder Sternberg and Charles drove into town for supplies. George and Levi continued work. George concentrated on some bones the team had begun to unearth, those of a duck-billed dinosaur.

'Finally by the evening of the third day,' he wrote later, 'I had traced the skeleton to the breast bone . . . when I removed a rather large piece of sandstone rock from over the breast, I found, much to my surprise, a perfect cast of the skin impression beautifully preserved. Imagine the feeling that crept over me when I realized that here for the first time a skeleton of a dinosaur had been discovered wrapped in its skin. That was a sleepless night for me. Had I missed my regular cup of coffee or eaten too many potatoes for supper?

'It was about dusk on the evening of the fifth day when we saw the wagon loaded with provisions roll into camp. "What luck?" was my father's first question. And before he could leave his seat I had given him a vivid sketch of my find . . . "Let's go and see it," he shouted as he jumped from his seat on the wagon. I grabbed some food from the boxes on the wagon and away the two of us went, leaving the others to prepare the meal for us. Darkness was nearly upon us when we reached the quarry and there laid out before us was the specimen. One glance was enough for my father to realize what I had found and what it meant to science. Will I ever forget his first remark as we stood there in the fast approaching twilight? It thrills me now as I repeat it. "George, this is a finer fossil than I have ever found. And the only thing which would have given me greater pleasure would have been to have discovered it myself." '

The dinosaur – an *Anatosaurus* – is now in the American Museum of Natural History in New York.

ANATOSAURUS SKIN IMPRESSION

flood, buried in sediment and fossilized. From this 'dinosaur mummy,' now in the American Museum of Natural History, New York, it is possible to see that the hand forms a sort of a paddle with webbing between the fingers and that the skin is covered with small rounded projections, or tubercles, with larger ones on the back and smaller ones on the underside. Perhaps this represents a color difference between the darker back and lighter side underneath.

The final group of bird-hipped dinosaurs was the ceratopsians ('horned-eye' or 'horned-face'). The first horn of a ceratopsian was found in 1887 and was indentified by Marsh as that of an extinct bison. Later one of

Edmontosaurus, **hadrosaurs with a flat head and the duck-bill which was typical of this widespread and successful family, stand in muddy shallows among the tough rushes upon which they may have fed.**

Marsh's collectors met a rancher, Charles Gurnsey, whose cowboys had found a great fossil 'with horns as long as a hoe handle and eye holes as big as your hat' sticking out of a bank on the side of a deep gulch. They had managed to loosen it and it had tumbled to the bottom of the gully with a tremendous crash and broken into several pieces. This second find confirmed to Marsh and his Yale colleagues that they were dealing with a new type of dinosaur. These, the horned dinosaurs, were the last of the great race of ruling reptiles to appear in the geological record; they appeared rapidly and evolved quickly into many different species, some with a formidable array of horns that make rhinos look positively docile. They were in addition confined to western North America and to eastern Asia, which were connected at the time but separated from the eastern parts of North America by sea.

The first recognizable ceratopsian is called *Protoceratops* ('first horned head') famous because of the range of its fossils that were found in Mongolia in the 1920s. In 1922 Roy Chapman Andrews' Central Asiatic Expedition of the American Museum of Natural History found fossil eggs of *Protoceratops* in the so-called Flaming Cliffs of the Gobi Desert. *Protoceratops* grew up to seven feet in length and was solidly quadrupedal, because it carried a very solid skull that was almost as long as its back. The weight was partly due to a heavy frill, or shield that extended back from the skull over the neck and shoulders. This frill, which characterized all the horned dinosaurs, had a number of functions. It acted as an attachment for the jaw and neck muscles, and provided protection for the neck and back. The skull itself had a parrot-like look to it, because the top jaw was hooked. But it also had a small bump on the midline of the nose – a foreshadowing of the horns that were to decorate its descendants.

The American Museum Expedition recovered some 70 eggs from the Flaming Cliffs and countless thousands of fragments. The eggs are about eight inches in length – larger relatively than any reptiles' eggs today – and very oblong, like the eggs of modern lizards. The shells had a speckled look and were probably leathery in life. The eggs were found in clutches and had obviously been set out in nests. Clearly *Protoceratops* females were comparable in their behavior to modern turtles: they dug hollows in the sand, deposited a dozen or so eggs in a circle and then covered the eggs with sand to hatch.

These were the first dinosaur eggs to be found (although some had been unearthed in France in the mid-nineteenth century and attributed to birds). Now, nine different types of dinosaur egg have been identified from both the Jurassic and Cretaceous. They mainly come from Mongolia and France, although others have been found in Brazil, the US and East Africa. One is associated with *Stegosaurus*.

All of these finds suggest some intriguing thoughts about how dinosaurs lived. The largest egg yet found belonged to a medium-sized, 35-foot Cretaceous sauropod from France, *Hypselosaurus*. The 12-inch long egg could contain about five and a half pints – twice the size of an ostrich egg but half the size of the largest known egg, that of the extinct Madagasan elephant bird, which was 28 inches around, about the limit in size for an egg. Beyond this point any shell, which must remain permeable to the gases that help nourish the embryo, collapses under gravitational pressure.

The odd thing about these eggs is the enormous disparity between the size of the hatchlings and the adult. An ostrich egg is about 1/60th the weight of the adult. An adult crocodile weighs 2000 times as much as its egg. *Hypselosaurus* would have had to multiply its weight perhaps 5000–10,000 times in growing up. Possible? And if so what of the giant sauropods? If they

The eggs of an early frilled dinosaur, *Protoceratops*, have been found in abundance in the Gobi. The eggs were laid in large pits in concentric circles. Possibly the female then covered the eggs with sand, as turtles do, and allowed the young to hatch out in the heat of the sun – a scene captured in the model below.

moved about in herds, what happened to the youngsters? Did they rear themselves from birth? Or did some sauropods simply drop live young, as many hoofed mammals do now, which would have joined the herd?

After *Proteceratops* the horned dinosaurs grew in size and developed their frills until there were two distinct families defined by long and short frills. The sequence is particularly well documented by the fossils found in the Cretaceous sediments of Wyoming, Montana and Alberta. Ten million years after *Protoceratops* lived, a single-horned rhinoceros-type creature called *Monoclonius* some 16 or 18 feet long, colonized North America. Some ten or 15 million years later still, the same area was home to *Triceratops* ('three-horned eye'), a massive 24-foot-long herbivore that weighed over eight tons. It had an enormous horn over each eye and a shorter one on its nose, and its bony neck frill reached well back over its shoulders. *Triceratops* must have filled a role comparable to a combination of buffalo and elephant, and wandered in herds of many thousands across the late Cretaceous landscapes of North America, probably surrounding their young to present a formidable battery of spikes for any would-be predators like *Tyrannosaurus*. 'Armed with long horns on a highly maneuverable head, strong beaks, and the ability to gallop at speeds probably up to 30 mph,' Bakker has written, 'these large ceratopsians must have been some of the most dangerous terrestrial herbivores ever to have evolved.' They survived right until the end of the dinosaurian times and then vanished rapidly.

The range of both the horned dinosaurs and the crested dinosaurs is somewhat baffling, yet their development parallels in some ways the immense range of antelopes in modern Africa which display a bewildering variety of sizes and apparently an inexplicable array of horns. Antelopes range from the minute dik-dik which is only one foot high at the shoulder to the 500-pound wildebeest. Altogether there are 110 species of this family with horns which are straight, curved, pronged, spiraled, twisted and curved forwards or backwards. Why? No one knows; and until we do, we shall have no true explanation of the variety of the late Cretaceous bird-hipped dinosaurs.

We have just reviewed an extraordinarily wide range of creatures. They include some of the most bizarre and extreme forms of terrestrial life the world has ever known. The 600 species now recognized by scientists – a necessarily vague figure – must represent only a fraction of those species that actually existed. New ones emerge regularly. Since the process of fossilization is random and limited in scope, it seems fair to guess that less than 10% of the actual number of dinosaur species have been found and identified. Some 3500 mammal species are known now. Since the dinosaurs did not colonize as many niches as successfully as modern mammals, there must have been fewer than that *at any one time*. But species arose and died out continuously over the 140-million year reign of the reptiles. If we include the other types of archosaur – the marine species and those that flew – and assume each species had a life-span of 10 million years, the number of species involved would approach 50,000. We are dealing then with a mode of life that was in its time as successful as that of the mammals that followed. (Of course we have no idea how long the mammals will last; perhaps 100 million years hence, some interstellar paleontologist of unimaginable shape and indescribable brilliance will conclude, with all the benefits of hindsight, that dinosaurs were in evolutionary terms, far more successful than us mammals.)

Comparable to mammals in their success – and comparable, too, in their physiology. They were built for efficient movement, with their legs set vertically beneath them, mammal-style. Many were clearly built for speed. But could they really move fast? Traditionally paleontologists said, 'No; they were reptiles.' But now many scientists argue: 'Yes; for they were not reptiles, at least not in the accepted sense of the word.' This is the central issue in the current debate about the dinosaurs.

The traditional view was summarized by Robert Bakker, who is in effect the spokesman of those who would have us look upon dinosaurs with new eyes, as follows: 'Paleontologists have assumed that in the everyday details of life, dinosaurs were merely overgrown alligators, or lizards. Crocodilians and lizards spend much of their time in inactivity, sunning themselves on a convenient rock or log and compared to modern mammals most modern reptiles are slow and sluggish. Hence the usual reconstruction of a dinosaur, such as *Brontosaurus*, is as a mountain of scaly flesh, which moved around only slowly and infrequently.' The very word 'saurus' – meaning a lizard or a reptile – suggests a comparison with modern reptiles. The popular image of dinosaurs is still that of some huge brute – its type does not matter very much – driven to extinction by changing circumstances to which it could not adapt because it was too cumbersome and stupid.

Yet even in Victorian terms, something is very wrong with this image. By the end of the century, it was widely known that dinosaurs ranged in size from small, apparently agile creatures the size of a goose up to the monumental sauropods. Clearly those with their legs tucked underneath them could not have been lizard-like. They were designed to run, and to run fast. As for the large ones, was it right to compare the physiology of a 'lizard' larger than an elephant with a lizard today?

Firstly what is usually meant by 'reptilian' physiology? Reptiles are described as 'cold-blooded.' This is an odd term, because no reptiles blood is actually cold. It is more accurate to say that they do not have the internal mechanisms to control their temperatures as mammals do, with a high metabolic rate and their own thermostatic regulators. Reptiles have to depend on the heat of the sun to warm them up. In technical terms they are ectotherms as opposed to the mammals which are endotherms.

This means that to control their internal temperatures – which they can do remarkably accurately – they have to adopt behavior that imposes severe limits on their way of life. For example in the Namib Desert of South-West Africa, there is a lizard that hunts in the heat of the day. The sand at midday is ferociously hot but the lizard has a neat way of counteracting its effects. First it lurks in the shadows of a large dune to lower its body temperature; then it dashes out into the glare of the sun on the scorching sands in pursuit of its insect prey. But it can only stand such conditions briefly. Whether or not it is successful in its hunt, it has to raise itself successively on to its toes, on to three legs, and finally on to two legs, lifting its tail as high as it can from the sand. Then scarcely touching the sand at all, and hence avoiding the effects of direct heat that would otherwise raise its internal temperature catastrophically, it scuttles back into the shadows on its rear legs, where it flattens itself against the cool ground to loose its excess heat as quickly as possible. After a few minutes it is ready for another foray. In cooler regions, lizards have to reverse this behavioral pattern: they must bask in the sun until their body reaches a proper temperature for efficient action.

Such behavior is all very well for small creatures. But could dinosaurs have lived in the same way? Quite simply, no. For larger creatures, it becomes increasingly difficult to preserve a stable internal temperature by relying on sun and shade. As size increases, mathematical realities take over.

Triceratops, 30 feet long and weighing eight tons, was the largest of its family and one of the last dinosaurs. The bony frill was, in early species, an attachment for powerful jaw muscles, but in later species it also probably served as a shield.

In its life-style, *Triceratops* may have combined the behavior of rhinoceroses and bisons. In this scene, males ring their herd to protect females and offspring

from the unwelcome attentions of a tyrannosaur, waiting for a chance to pick out a likely kill.

As an example, take a cube 2″ × 2″ × 2″; its volume is eight cubic inches; the combined surface area of its six sides is 24 square inches. In pure numerical terms therefore, the relationship between volume and surface area is 8:24, or in other terms 1:3. Now double the size of the cube, so that each side is four inches. The volume goes up to 64 cubic inches (4″ × 4″ × 4″); note that the sides have doubled but the original volume (8) has now *squared*. And the surface area of all its six sides is 96 square inches (4″ × 4″ × 6″). So the surface area of the first cube (24 square inches) has gone up only four times. But the ratio of volume to surface area has changed. From 1:3, it now stands at 2:3. In other words there is a lot more relatively on the inside; less, relatively, is exposed to the air; and heat will flow in and out more slowly.

Shortly after the Second World War, a number of scientists, among them the dinosaur expert, Edwin Colbert, did some experiments with alligators in Florida to see how this worked in practice. They found that larger alligators when tied up out in the sun became hotter more slowly than smaller ones. A tiny alligator raised its temperature 1°C in only one and a half minutes. A 30-pounder needed seven and a half minutes for the same rise. On the same analogy, a large dinosaur, say a ten-tonner, would take almost four days *in continuous sunshine* to raise its body temperature by 1°C. This is clearly absurd. Not even in Florida does the sun shine that long.

Even if these conclusions were wrong – and the original experts did in fact revise their opinions somewhat later – the general point still holds. If a dinosaur lost heat overnight, it would have to regain it the next day but regular basking in the sun could not achieve this because the heat would not have a chance to spread through the vast bulk of flesh from the skin to the inside of the body. To raise the *internal* temperature significantly the skin would have to be subjected to heat so intense that it would burn it away completely. Large adult dinosaurs must, therefore, have sustained a stable temperature simply as a consequence of their size. In other words they had no need of the internal regulatory system that mammals and birds have. At the time, this did not seem all that surprising a conclusion, for it was assumed that the world was a uniformly warm place and the dinosaurs would not have cooled significantly overnight, and would not need to sunbathe the following day.

The large dinosaurs, then, were not to be compared with lizards today. But what of the smaller ones? And *was* the climate uniformly warm enough to sustain reptilian efficiency? And were the dinosaurs really so limited in their activities as the lizard-image suggested?

In 1969 two eminent scientists, John Ostrom of Yale and Armand de Ricqlès at Paris University, both arrived at similar conclusions, that approached these questions from another angle. Ostrom pointed out that lizards and other reptiles spend a very high proportion of their lives stationary because they cannot sustain extended activity, whereas mammals and birds are active for most of their waking life. A rat burns energy at ten times the rate of a crocodile. This activity is the result of the high metabolic rate that goes hand-in-hand with their efficient upright gait. Dinosaurs were upright; would they not therefore have had the metabolism to use their bodies to the maximum? They were, he thought, relatively independent of external temperatures. 'The correlation of high body temperature ... high metabolism, and erect posture and locomotion is not accidental. [They] probably are not possible without high metabolism and high uniform temperature.'

De Ricqlès, meanwhile, pointed out that one indicator of a high metabolism was a particular type of bone physiology. Bone is a complex living

Dinosaur Rush to the Gobi

In the early 1920s dinosaur hunters turned their attention from America to the Far East. They did so because it had been suggested that Central Asia might be the original homeland of the early mammals and of man himself. Fired by this idea, Roy Chapman Andrews, who was on the staff of the American Museum of Natural History, began to dream of an expedition on a grand scale to Central Asia, particularly to Mongolia and its huge expanse of grassland and desert, the Gobi.

He set out to look for man's ancestors – a wild gamble but it paid off in a completely unforeseen way that has made Mongolia a Mecca for dinosaur-hunters ever since.

Andrews faced formidable obstacles. No paleontological work had ever been done in Mongolia. Food and water were scarce, and in winter temperatures dropped to −40°F. Success would have to come in the summer months and, to be certain of it, a whole team of trained specialists would have to be taken into virtually unknown territory in a convoy of trucks and cars.

To solve the problems, Andrews thought big. To get enough petrol, tyres, spare parts, clothing, food, water, scientific equipment and trained personnel into and out of Mongolia at the same time, he planned on using both camels and cars. The camels would act as a base line, marching directly across the desert, carrying thousands of gallons of petrol and oil, and tons of flour, rice and other food. The cars would zig-zag across the desert at high speed, covering immense amounts of territory and meeting up with the camel train at pre-arranged places to stock up with supplies and make repairs.

Although the first year was meant to be for reconnaissance only, it proved rapidly and brilliantly successful. Speeding across the Gobi to complete the first year's survey before the onset of winter, the expedition came across a large eroded basin of red sandstone, consisting of high sculptured cliffs, which glowed so dramatically in the setting sun that they were called the Flaming Cliffs. At the foot of these cliffs, the fossil hunters found a number of bones and some fossilized shells of oblong eggs. They were those of primitive ceratopsians, whose fossil remains were found nearby.

The next year, the expedition returned to the Flaming Cliffs, which proved a treasure trove. Work continued there for the next two seasons. In that time, the team discovered more than 100 specimens of *Protoceratops*, ranging from babies to adults. And, of course, there were eggs by the score. Other discoveries were made – of an armored dinosaur, of coelurosaurs, of primitive mammals and of other ancient reptiles, many similar to those unearthed in North America. The finds proved that once North America and Asia were joined and that dinosaurs could wander back and forth between the two continents.

Andrew's discoveries also pointed the way to later expeditions by Mongolian, Russian and Polish paleontologists after the Second World War. One of these – the 1970 Polish-Mongolian expedition – proved particularly successful. One find was of two small dinosaurs apparently locked in a struggle to the death. Another was a fine specimen of a local tyrannosaur, *Tarbosaurus bataar*, which was excavated and transported with equipment of which Andrews would surely have been envious.

Andrews – toting a revolver as a precaution against brigands – kneels with an assistant beside a clutch of dinosaur eggs.

Among the finds made by the Polish-Mongolian expedition into the Gobi in 1970 was the skeleton of a tyrannosaur named *Tarbosaurus bataar* (left). Here, paleontologists excavate the pelvic bones. Below, expedition members slide a crate packed with bones down towards a truck, prior to transporting the discoveries back to Ulan Bator, the Mongolian capital.

tissue; it helps in the formation of blood cells and the maintenance of the balance between calcium and phosphate, both vital to nerve and muscle function. A bone's micro-structure can thus reflect body chemistry as a whole. In mammals and birds, the blood vessels permeating the bones are densely packed and so are the sites that control the exchange of calcium and phosphate between skeleton and blood. Reptiles' bones show a much lower level of activity. Given a tight correlation between bone structure and metabolism – a correlation that is by no means proven – dinosaurs bones would be more mammalian than reptilian.

The main proponent of the warm-bloodedness of dinosaurs is Bob Bakker, now at Harvard. His views were first stated in an article in *Nature* in 1972 and then restated to a wider audience in *The Scientific American* in April 1975 in an article significantly entitled 'Dinosaur Renaissance.' He argued as follows:

Dinosaurs look as if they are designed for speed (or rather many of them do). Their legs are tucked well underneath the bodies like mammals and they have long legs. There would be no point in such adaptations unless the creatures were capable of sustained activity, rather than operating in short bursts as, for instance, lizards do. Following the mammalian model, some dinosaurs should have been able to reach maximum speeds of over 40 mph (many hoofed herbivores – like antelopes – have been timed at well over 40 mph, as have their predators).

Bakker also points to the analysis of bone structure and then brings in an argument all his own. It is based on the amount of food needed by a mammal as opposed to a reptile. Because of their lower metabolic rate, reptiles, he argues, need to consume only two or three times their own body weight each year. In a balanced community if you add up the total weight of all the predatory lizards and then add up the total weights of all their prey, the lizards will weigh about 40% of their prey. Mammals, however, need to consume anything between ten and 100 times their own weight every year, depending on their size. (The larger the creature, the less it needs in proportion – a shrew consumes 100 times it own weight every year, and a lion ten times its own weight.)

This is such a significant difference, Bakker says, that it should be reflected in the fossil record. Assuming that this is in fact so, it is possible to assess the total weights of predators and their prey, compare them and thus establish whether the predators were reptilian or mammalian. For example in remains from the early Permian, of Texas, 40%–50% of the bones represent fossils of *Dimetrodon*. The rest of the bones represent a variety of species upon which *Dimetrodon* preyed. Yet in the Jurassic Morrison Beds of the American West, the remains of the principal predator, *Allosaurus*, represent just 2 or 3% of the combined weights of the various preys – *Stegosaurus*, *Camarasaurus* and

This diagram shows why a large dinosaur could preserve a stable internal temperature and thus possibly sustain a mammal-like metabolism. In a small creature, represented by a single cube, all parts are near the surface. In a large creature, the same volume of flesh is insulated by the rest of the body. A sauropod could neither gain nor lose heat rapidly.

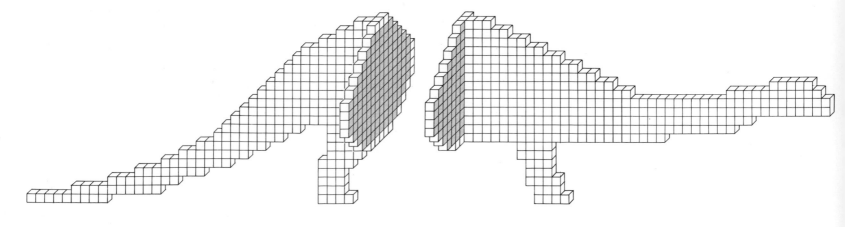

Diplodocus. Clearly Bakker argues, *Allosaurus* needed to eat a lot more and must, therefore, have had a high metabolic rate.

Bakker extends his evidence to many different fossil beds in Mexico, Texas, South Africa, Zambia, Tanzania, Russia, China and Europe. He shows powerfully the change in the predator-prey ratios that marked the early ectothermic – or 'cold-blooded' – reptilian communities (40%–50%), the later mammal-like reptiles and thecodonts (10%–20%), and the dinosaur communities (below 5%).

It will take some time for scientists to reach any sort of a consensus on these arguments. For one thing fossilization is pretty much a matter of luck. Do the finds represent a proper cross section of any community? It may be, that allosaurs in the Late Jurassic were simply not fossilized as much as their prey for some reason or other. Such 'distortions' in the fossil record are known to occur. In the La Brea district of Los Angeles, paleontologists have excavated tar-pits which 15,000 years ago trapped many hundreds of mammals. Of the remains, most are carnivores; yet in life the herbivores must have been in the majority.

Again – as Alan Charig at the British Museum (Natural History) argues – it might also be that allosaurs lived many times longer than their prey; perhaps allosaur corpses only became available for fossilization every 100 years as opposed to every ten years for the creatures upon which they preyed. Moreover even if Bakker is right his arguments apply only to predators not prey.

The arguments still need a lot of evidence and a lot of refining. The experts should be arguing happily about the conclusions for years to come but it seems fairly certain that the dinosaurs deserve our respect as a pretty advanced form of life. They could have represented a departure as radical as that of the reptiles and the mammals, as different from those two as they are from each other.

If Bakker has his way, these suggestions will one day be accepted as facts, and scientists will have to revise the whole system of classification. At present, dinosaurs are still labeled as reptiles. They should not be, argues Bakker. The archosaurs deserve a class of their own, on a par with reptiles and mammals, and it should start with the thecodonts which invented 'warm-bloodedness.'

This has one particularly odd implication. Birds, it is generally agreed, originated from thecodonts. So did the dinosaurs. Birds and dinosaurs are, therefore, in Bakker's view, close relatives. Indeed he believes that dinosaurs, not thecodonts, were the direct ancestors of birds. So the birds no longer deserve such reverential treatment by classifiers, and should be demoted to become an order of the archosaurs. 'The dinosaurs are not extinct. The colorful and successful diversity of the living birds is a continuing expression of basic dinosaur physiology.'

At first sight there does not seem much in common between a duck and a *Diplodocus* and few people could at present imagine a humming-bird as a distant relative of *Tyrannosaurus.* But then who would suspect a whale and a shrew of being members of the same class? However surprising it may seem, by looking a little more closely at the birds and their origins, we may come to understand a little more about the dinosaurs and their natures.

In this 1836 view popularizing the recent discovery of the Age of Reptiles, an ichthyosaur devours a plesiosaur amidst a welter of predatory carnage.

5/Rulers of Sea and Air

The success of the great reptiles was not limited to the land. Early in their evolution they recolonized the seas and took to the air. The sea-dwellers were not all that closely related to the dinosaurs – they evolved long before even the earliest dinosaurs had emerged – but they are very much part of the dinosaur story, for the large marine reptiles died out at the same time as the dinosaurs themselves and any account of their extinction must take the disappearance of the marine reptiles into account as well.

The flyers are also of significance because the birds stem from them. Indeed a number of scientists believe that the early birds were so similar to some of the smaller dinosaurs that the two must have been directly related and that the birds are in fact the only surviving descendants of the dinosaurs.

The three major groups of marine reptiles were already well known in the nineteenth century: the dolphin-like ichthyosaurs, the plesiosaurs, and the mosasaurs.

No one yet knows how ichthyosaurs evolved. These sleek, finned reptiles bore little apparent relationship to any of the land-based forms described so far. Their bodies were superbly adapted to the marine environment, streamlined and tipped with a long, pointed snout. Their limbs, though containing their full complement of reptilian bones, were compressed and flattened into front and rear flippers. Many species had vicious sets of teeth and they must have lived by hunting – probably fish, squid and cuttlefish.

The rear end of the backbone had a strange downward kink in it. At first this was thought to be the result of some disturbance of the skeleton after death and several species were mounted with the backbone straightened out. Later it was realized that the backbone kinked down to act as a strut for the lower part of the tail, which in later species looked identical to that of a dolphin. The evolution of this efficient means of propulsion can be clearly seen from the fossil record: the earliest ichthyosaurs had a tail with only a small kink and which was formed with one dominant, powerful fin; later species showed an abrupt kink and a tail of two equal lobes.

Since they were so utterly adapted to life in water ichthyosaurs could not come out on to the land; they must therefore have given birth to their young alive, as dolphins do. Some particularly fine ichthyosaur skeletons have been found in Holzmaden, in Baden – Württemberg, West Germany, some of which contain unborn young; and there is even one skeleton in which the mother and child have been fossilized, by some extraordinary circumstance, at the moment of birth.

The ichthyosaurs evolved during the Triassic and the early ones were contemporaries of strange creatures called nothosaurs. Nothosaurs looked like giant carnivorous newts, with tails that were flattened to act as paddles and webbed feet. They must have been shallow water marine predators who returned to land to breed (indeed their young have been found in plenty in caves near the primeval Tethys coast). Though rather primitive looking creatures, they were in fact extraordinarily successful and inhabited coast-lines from Europe to Japan, lazing on rocks as seals do today.

Their probable descendants were the plesiosaurs, which were fully aquatic, with large flippers and long reptilian necks. Plesiosaur means 'near-reptile,' for it was once thought that they were creatures in the throes of evolving into reptiles from aquatic animals. The largest ones measured between 40 and 50 feet long. They must have moved somewhat as turtles do now, rowing themselves along with their flattened limbs. They were once referred to as swan-lizards but there was little of the swan about them (though one type of plesiosaur was *Elasmosaurus*, the creature with the 23-foot neck whose vertebrae Cope got round the wrong way). Dean Buckland more aptly described the plesiosaur as a turtle with a snake strung through it. The turtle

Plesiosaur skeletons, when mounted in museums often look those of cumbersome creatures. *Brachauchenus's* skull was a massive five feet long and *Trinacromerum*, a Late Cretaceous plesiosaur, seems ungainly and tanklike. In fact, the plesiosaurs, along with many other groups of marine reptiles, were extraordinarily successful: they dominated the warm coastal seas of the Age of Reptiles for over 100 million years.

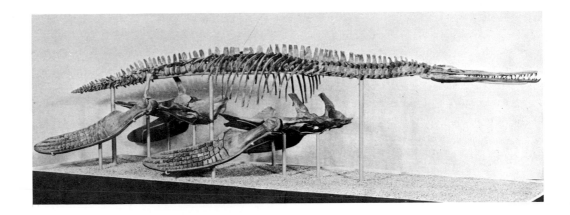

image was unwittingly accurate; no young have been found inside plesiosaur skeletons, suggesting the notion that they led a turtle-like existence, returning to the shores to lay eggs. If so, a Jurassic shore might have seen the heavy females laboring up the beach on their paddles to bury eggs that would have hatched safely a foot or two down, releasing young plesiosaurs an inch or two long to scrabble and tumble their way down to the sea.

Plesiosaurs, which have acquired some recent notoriety as suggested candidates to explain the Loch Ness Monster, evolved in one branch into short-necked versions known as pliosaurs, which developed remarkably heavy heads and may have lived, as sperm-whales do today, largely on cuttlefish. The pliosaurs culminated in a monster of some note, *Kronosaurus*, whose 13-foot skull gave it the largest head of any reptile.

The mosasaurs were the largest lizards ever, as well as being fully marine. They looked like a plesiosaur crossed with a crocodile. They probably used their long necks to seize passing fish, or even an unwary *Pteranodon*, drifting along a few inches clear of the surface in its search for small fry. They were in fact quite closely related to present-day monitor lizards, though the fact was disguised by the shape of their tail, which was flattened like an oar for swimming, and by their limbs, which were short paddles with webbed fingers and toes. They were also large – up to 50 feet, compared with the 10–12 feet of today's largest monitor, the Komodo dragon. Mosasaurs had huge jaws, the lower halves of which were jointed (like monitors' jaws), to allow them to separate at the hinge (as monitors' jaws do), to allow it to swallow massive chunks of food. They probably hunted almost anything that moved. They

This restoration (bottom) shows a mosasaur, perhaps the most rapacious predator of late Cretaceous seas, in the act of seizing an ammonite, an extinct squid-like creature encased in a spiral shell. The evidence for this incidence comes from the ammonite in question (below), which shows the marks of teeth that match a mosasaur jaw-line.

146

certainly crunched up ammonites, extinct squid-like creatures protected by a shell. One ammonite shell, punctured by mosasaur teeth, shows evidence of such an encounter; the mosasaur seized its prey, bit into it several times, failed to swallow it, dropped it, picked it up again and this time succeeded in tearing out the soft parts, which it consumed, leaving the shell to sink to the ocean floor, where it was fossilized.

No young mosasaurs have ever been found, although adult fossils are common enough. It has been suggested that the females went up rivers to breed and that the young remained in fresh water until old enough to fend for themselves in the open sea.

The tiny Bornean flying-lizard, *Draco* (below), bears a striking resemblance to the Triassic glider, *Icarosaurus* (right). *Icarosaurus* probably used its extended ribs with their membranous coverings to glide from tree to tree, tucking its 'wings' away when at rest.

None of these creatures belonged to the archosaurs, the group that includes the dinosaurs proper. Only one archosaur species reconquered the sea. These were the sea-crocodiles, some of which grew up to a fearsome 50 feet in length. They ate squids and octopuses (fossilized stomach stones, or gastroliths, of sea-crocodiles have been found that seem to bear the traces of squid 'ink'). Yet for some reason the sea-crocodiles did not make the grade: they did not survive even to the end of the Cretaceous.

The sea-going reptiles that did survive – and still do – were the turtles. These seem immune to change (although the age of reptiles did throw up its usual record – *Archelon*, a turtle with a shell ten feet long). They have remained much the same for the past 200 million years – a permanent warning for those who would write off any creature as 'primitive.'

Besides conquering the land and reinvading the sea, the archosaurs also took to the air. They did so in at least four different ways: as parachutists; as four-legged gliders; as winged reptiles – and finally as birds.

The first known flier was an early Triassic humming-bird-sized lizard called *Longisquama* ('long scale'). This tiny creature – which may, when its affinities are known, turn out to be the smallest archosaur known – had issuing from its back two banks of filmy scales that it presumably spread out to either side to act as something between a wing and a parachute. If these were primitive wings, they were of a very special sort, for they did not issue from the fore-limbs and cannot therefore count as the original versions of the wings that later evolved on birds themselves.

The second early flyer was the mouse-sized *Podopteryx* ('foot wing'), which possessed flaps of skin between the fore and rear limbs, and between the rear limbs to the base of the tail. It must have looked something like a modern flying lizard (except that Borneo's several species of *Draco* have 'wings' supported by extended ribs, making it a sort of hybrid, in its mode of flying, of *Longisquama* and *Podopteryx*). *Podopteryx* must – like *Draco* – have spread its membranes in a flash of color to glide from tree to tree.

These two creatures, found in the 1960s in Kirgizia by the Russian paleontologist, A Sharov, are so extraordinary – if only for their size – that new families have been created to accommodate them.

Nor were these two types alone, even in Triassic times. There were other gliding lizards which *did* evolve membranous extensions from their ribs (one of them is named, suitably enough, *Icarosaurus* after the mythical Greek who built himself prototype wings).

The relationship between these various creatures is obscure but it seems likely that the *Podopteryx* was a predecessor to the later pterosaurs, or 'flying lizards.' As pterosaurs evolved, the leading membrane – that between the front and rear limbs – became increasingly important, until it became a proper wing, supported by the forearm, hand and a spindly fourth finger.

The first pterosaur – or pterodactyl ('winged finger') as pterosaurs used to be known – was found in 1784 in the Bavarian limestone of Eichstätt by an Italian naturalist, Cosmo Alessandro Collini, who was the curator of the museum at Mannheim. Collini thought it was a ray-like fish; others that it was a combination of a bird and a bat. But Cuvier pointed out that its vertebrae and legs were those of a lizard and that it was definitely reptilian. He also remarked its oddities – a long snout, toothed, with clawed fingers half way along its wing.

The first English pterosaur was unearthed in 1828 by Mary Anning. She

This mid-nineteenth century restoration of pterosaurs shows them as hairy and bat-like. Pterosaurs were, however, rapidly classed as reptiles and the possibility that any reptile could have hair was generally discounted. Now, it is known that pterosaurs *were* hairy, and the reptilian classification seems strange.

presented it to William Buckland, who was amazed at the find. It was, he said, 'a monster resembling nothing that has ever been seen or heard of on earth excepting the dragons of romance, or heraldry.' Though accepting the idea that it was a flyer, he was puzzled by the claws and believed it must have been able to climb trees. To cap it all, he also suggested it could swim; it was, he said, 'all qualified for all services and all elements.'

By the mid century, however, pterosaurs were generally recognized as flying creatures. Owen pictured them as cumbersome flying reptiles that looked like a cross between griffins and turkeys. In his reconstructions their legs are too heavy, their bodies too big and their wings too small. He was understandably puzzled by them. There is, he said, 'a physiological improbability that the cold-blooded organization of a reptile should be able to raise a larger mass into the air than could be done by the warm-blooded mammals.'

Owen underestimated both their aerodynamic and (almost certainly) their metabolic capacities. Towards the end of the nineteenth century, it was realized that the pterosaur was neatly built, intelligent and fast moving. In many ways they were comparable to birds.

Like birds, many species had short, broad wings that characterized flapping flight. They needed similar co-ordinating abilities, linked to an acute sense of vision. This meant that their brain was remarkably bird-like. Unlike a normal reptilian brain, a pterosaur's brain completely fills its brain

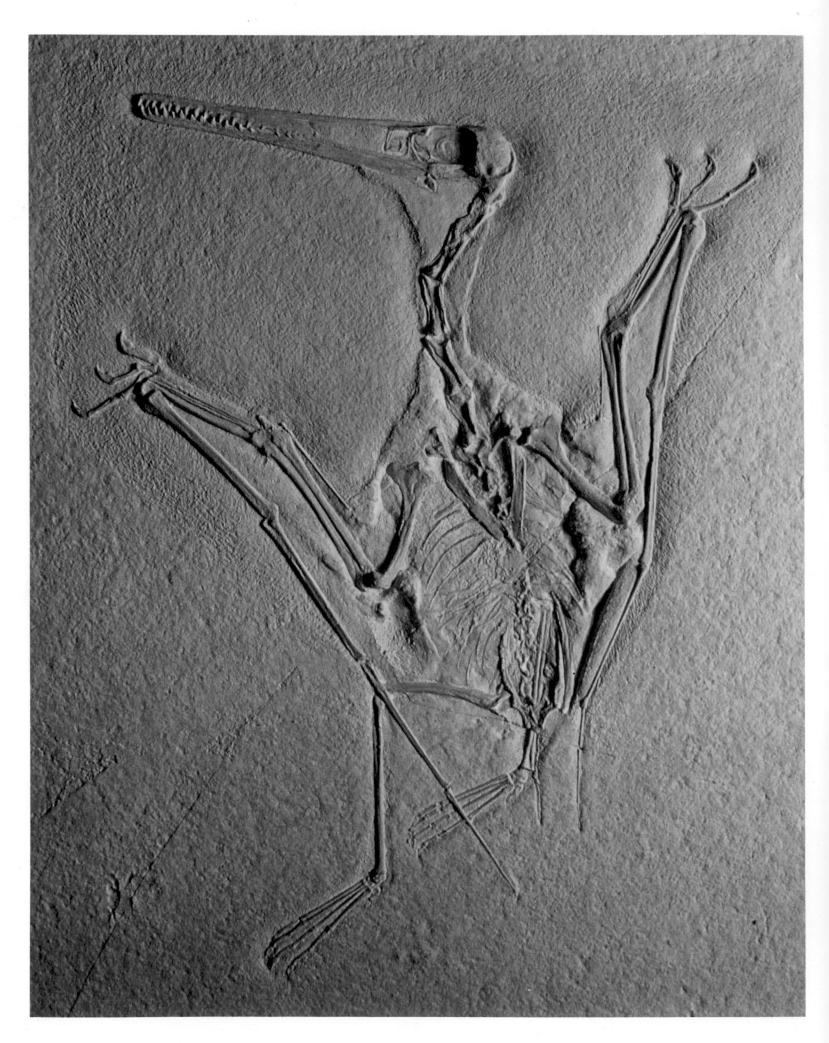

Although pterosaurs are normally restored as rather unappealing creatures, these two skeletons (left and right) from Solnhofen, Bavaria, reveal the beauty and delicacy of their structure. The claws and teeth that characterize them are clearly in evidence.

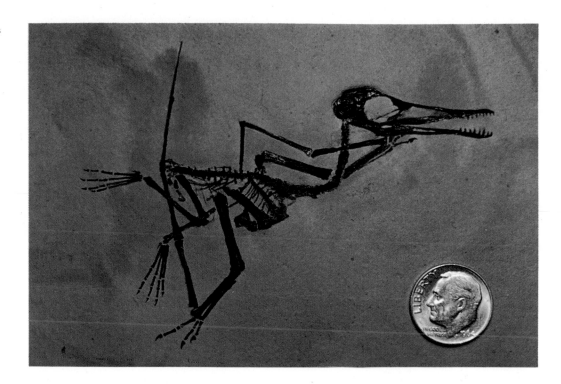

case. In some species the case – enlarged to accommodate the brain – is a dome of bone. The cerebellum at the back, which controls movement and balance and is not normally well developed in reptiles, is clearly of great importance to birds and pterosaurs. The optic lobes, of the mid-brain, which co-ordinate vision and are not normally well developed in dinosaurs, are huge in pterosaurs and bear a striking resemblance to those of birds. It seems likely that to develop bird-like behavior, the pterosaurs had bird-like intelligence.

Their respiratory systems were probably bird-like as well. Powered flight demands a good deal of energy. Their muscles would have needed to be as efficient as those of birds. Perhaps their metabolism was comparable to that of birds in others ways as well. Birds breathe differently from mammals. They have no diaphragm, relying instead on the expansion and contraction of the muscles of the body-wall to force air in and out. In addition to supply the

The pterosaur, *Pterodactylus*, with its thin leathery wings was reminiscent of a modern fruit-bat with a long beak.

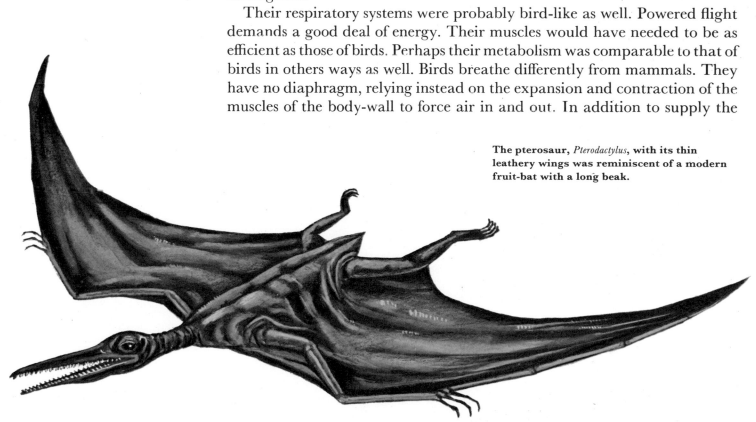

oxygen they need, they have air-sacs that extend into their bones (some species even have air-sacs in their toes). How birds actually make use of their air-sacs is a matter of some conjecture but it is certain that they assist in processing inhaled air and also help in cooling (birds do not sweat). Pterosaurs, like birds, possessed small openings into their hollow bones and their physiology may have been equally complex and equally efficient.

Given all this, why then should they be classed as reptiles? Surely, their high metabolism is completely non-reptilian? This problem was quite apparent in the nineteenth century. In 1901 Harry Govier Seeley summarized the finds in his *Dragons of the Air*, the first book devoted exclusively to pterosaurs. The pterosaurs, he pointed out, must have been intelligent fast-moving and with high endurance – for they were not presumably rapidly grounded by exhaustion as a flying lizard would be – and they would surely have had a four-chambered heart to avoid a reptilian circulation, in which the oxygen-rich arterial blood is diluted with oxygen-deficient venous blood. The conclusion, accepted by a number of scientists, was that pterosaurs must have been warm-blooded like mammals and birds (though even if this idea becomes widely adopted pterosaurs are bound to be classed as reptiles for many years to come).

In that case they must also have been insulated. All small creatures with a high metabolic rate – mammals and birds alike – need insulation. There are no naked birds and very few small hairless mammals.

In 1927 a German paleontologist, Ferdinand Broili, insisted that pterosaurs were covered with fine hair. He compared the skin of the bat to the skin impressions of a pterosaur and found them very similar. But positive proof of this idea has only recently emerged. In 1970 A G Sharov of the Soviet Academy of Sciences, found a small pterosaur beautifully preserved in lake deposits at Karatay, Kazakhstan. The fine-grained rock showed delicate details like the wing membranes – and a furry pelt so clear that individual hairs could be seen. There was even hair on the fingers half way along the front edge of the wing and on the membranes between the toes. Sharov called his discovery *Sordes pilosus* ('filthy fur').

In their reproductive behavior too, pterosaurs were possibly bird-like. They may well have laid eggs, like their reptilian ancestors. Even if they brought forth their young alive, however, they would have needed to expend considerable care on keeping their offspring warm and feeding them. They must have paired, nested, lived in colonies – in fact, done many of the things that modern birds to.

There was one other characteristic of some pterosaur species that makes them remarkable: their size. In 1871 Marsh announced the discovery of a pterosaur over 20 feet across. He named it *Pteranodon* ('winged and toothless'). It had a long toothless beak balanced by an elongated bony crest jutting back from the top of the skull. It was found in marine sediments and was a coast-dweller. Its body was no longer than that of a turkey and with a span of up to 25 feet it really was all wing.

It also had strange trailing hind limbs which would have made landing ungainly. It is hard to imagine how they could ever have landed. It was suggested, early in the century, that they crash-landed on their stomachs and then somehow shunted themselves along with their reversed hind limbs, supporting themselves on the clawed front limbs situated halfway along their wings. Once safely down, it was thought that *Pteranodon* could have used its back legs to hang in bat-like fashion from rocky ledges, dropping off to ride the air-currents out to sea, where it fed on fish.

The flight mechanisms of the *Pteranodon* were remarkable; at first it was not appreciated just how amazing. Owen, for instance, assumed that the atmosphere in Cretaceous times must have been denser in order to give such weighty creatures proper support. In fact no such assumptions are necessary; *Pteranodon* was a flight engineer's dream. Every part of its skeleton was designed for a combination of lightness and strength to solve the aerodynamic problems posed by its size.

There has never been much question about the flying abilities of small pterosaurs; but large ones faced considerable difficulties and the larger they were, the severer the problems. Birds face the same problems. As size increases, weight goes up even faster, for a larger body needs broader wings, which demand a whole range of back-up systems – muscle, bones, heart, lungs, digestive tract. The effects are dramatic. When size is doubled – assuming shape and structure remain in proportion – weight increases *eightfold*. Other factors, like the strain on the wings and power-requirements, increase in proportions that are similarly imposing. This means that the larger the flying creature, the more subtle its weight-saving engineering has to be. Theoretically, the interaction between these elements allows engineers to calculate an upper limit to pterosaur size. Until recently, *Pteranodon* was thought to represent that limit.

In *Pteranodon* the reduction in weight seems to have been taken to its logical conclusion. Scaling up a bird in proportion puts *Pteranodon's* weight at some 100 kilos (200 pounds). In fact it weighed only 17 kilos (35 pounds). Only 30% of its skeleton was solid; the rest was taken up with air-sacs. Its wing-

Pteranodons **swoop and scrabble round their cliff-based eyries. Though** *Pteranodons* **were probably gull-like in their habits, it is unclear how they coped with their delicate, kite-like, 25-foot wing span when landing on rocky surfaces.**

Perhaps the most extraordinary thing about *Pteranodon* (**left**), **thought until the 1970s to be** the largest flying creature ever, was its skull (**below**). Four-foot long, it was designed to carry long, pelican-like beak used for fishing. An immense crest (which varied in shape between species) jutted out two feet from its skull. Wind-tunnel tests have shown that this device acted to counteract the air pressure on *Pteranodon's* beak when it turned its head sideways.

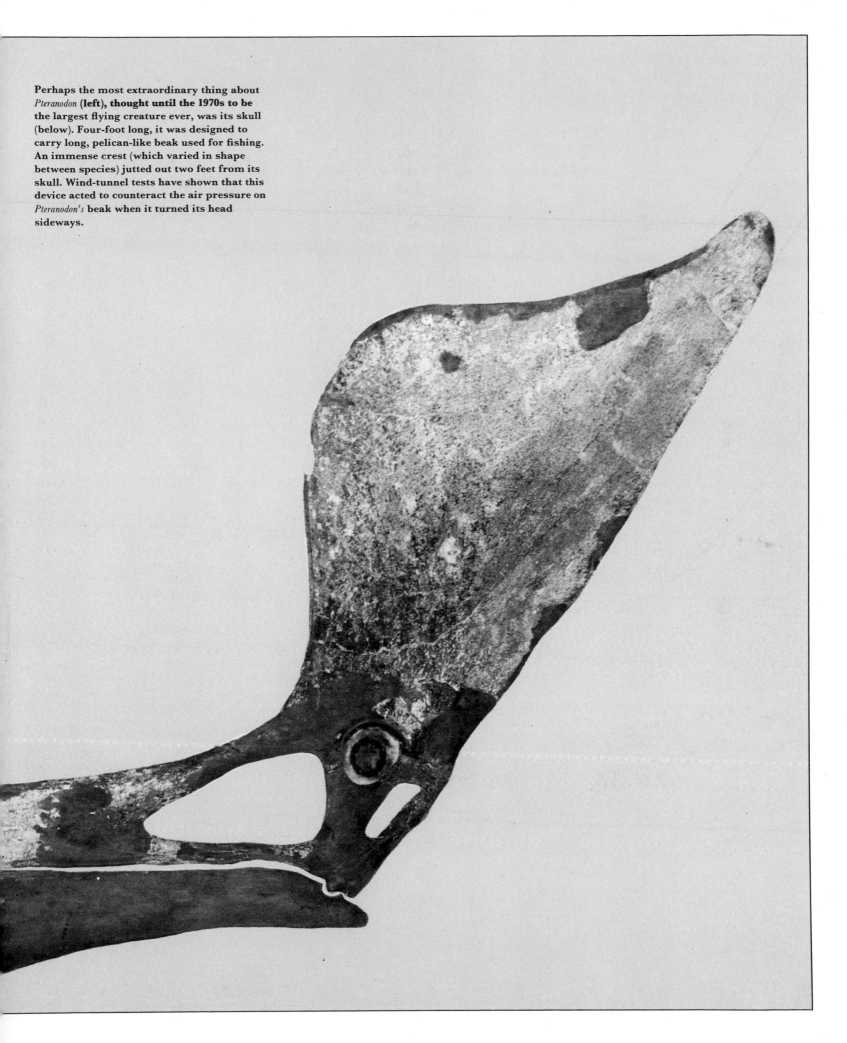

bones, back-bone and hind-limbs were tubular, like aircraft struts. All its bones were of eggshell delicacy – in some cases their walls were an unbelievable $\frac{1}{25}$ of an inch thick, as was the membrane of its wings. It must have floated along as lightly as a kite.

In a 1974 study by two English scientists, Cherrie Bramwell and George Whitfield of Reading University, *Pteranodon* is seen as the ultimate in gliding efficiency. It would hardly need to flap at all, they agreed. It took off by dropping away from its cliff-side nest to drift easily over the waves, whose updrafts supported it as it dipped its head for fish. Updrafts at cliff-faces would take it back to its nesting place again. Even the crest was seen as a marvelous adaptation to avoid extra muscle power. It needed a long beak to fish but such a beak had one disadvantage: if *Pteranodon* turned its head sideways, air pressure on the beak would have demanded powerful neck muscles to turn the head back to the forward position. The crest avoided the need for extra neck muscles – its large surface area acted as an automatic stabilizer. When the head was turned the pressure on the beak was balanced by a corresponding pressure on the crest which brought the head into the forward position again. The crest weighed only 30 grams (an ounce or two) but to achieve the same effect with muscle would have demanded 200 grams (half a pound) of flesh.

Pteranodon would have glided at about 15 miles an hour and at that speed it would have been a better glider than any bird. Its wings locked into a gliding position with a special adaptation of the joint. But – and it is a big but – Bramwell and Whitfield argued that the *Pteranodon* could never have had muscle enough to flap. It was, they said, 'obviously near to the upper limit of flying size for pterosaurs.' For purely physical reasons, the *Pteranodon's* performance if extrapolated from that of a bird, leads into the realms of impossibility.

To understand this demands a further exploration of the dynamics of flapping flight. If the mass of a bird doubles, its wing span must go up by a factor of three. This is fine for gliders but not for those creatures wishing to attempt powered flight. With increasing wing span, the number of flaps per second falls and the power of the muscles – given the fact that they must all be

A How-to of Pteranodon Flight

The flying abilities of *Pteranodon* have long been a matter of controversy. It seemed too weak to flap, and thus to take off or sustain powered flight. And its legs, which pointed backwards to form bat-like claws, seemed the wrong shape for landing. These sketches suggest how it may have overcome these apparent problems.

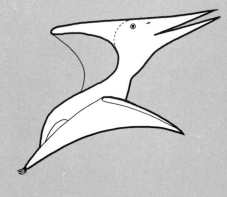

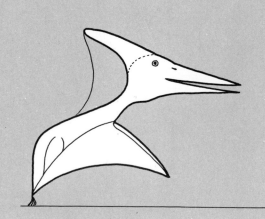

Pteranodon was so lightly built that single flap from an upright position (left) was enough to achieve take-off. Experiments have shown that a wing-beat cycle of one beat per second – well within its capacities – was enough to sustain its 11 mph flying speed (above).

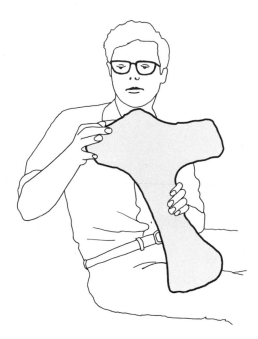

This drawing indicates the scale of the 17-inch *Quetzalcoatlus* wing-bone, with its huge bulge to which the wing muscles attached.

tucked in near the body – must be more than squared. But as muscle power increases, the strain on the wing increases disproportionately. Heavier bones are required; which demand correspondingly heavier muscles; which increase the bulk of the body; which again demands more wing area, and yet heavier bones, and yet more muscle.

All these effects react on each other, defining an effective upper limit for powered flight. Icarus, the mythical Greek hero who built wings which collapsed in the heat of the sun, would never have got air-borne. He would have needed a wing-span of 50 feet or so simply to glide, and to flap wings 50 feet across powerfully enough to lift a man's weight would demand muscles so massive that the width of the wings would actually need to increase to several hundred feet . . . and so on. Clearly, argued Bramwell and Whitfield, no flying creature could exist much larger than *Pteranodon*.

But such conclusions are risky. Nature is more ingenious than the equations give credit for. There was a famous mathematical analysis of a bumble-bee which proved conclusively that bees cannot fly. Bramwell and Whitfield may well have under-estimated the efficiency of the *Pteranodon's* flight. Ross Stein at Brown University, Providence, Rhode Island, who has done extensive wind tunnel tests on model *Pteranodon* wings, certainly believes so. In a study published in 1975 Stein, who likes sailing and to whom the analogy came quite naturally, compared *Pteranodon's* wings to the sail of a yacht. A yacht's sail when tacking hard into the wind adopts a shape that is *not* ideal for a glider, held taut as it is along the bottom edge by the boom. In the case of *Pteranodon* the 'booms' are represented by its body and back legs. The 'sail' (or wing) tends to billow upwards and outwards increasingly as it nears the tip. In a gliding creature like the *Pteranodon* this effect progressively altered the angle at which the membrane struck the air along the length of the wing. This meant that in gliding, lift also varied along the wing, decreasing gliding efficiency (birds have complicated aero-dynamic and muscular methods of counteracting this effect).

If *Pteranodon* could have flapped, however, it could have overcome this effect. In flapping flight, lift is achieved by the forward swing of the wings which pivots from the shoulder socket, so that the tip moves faster through the

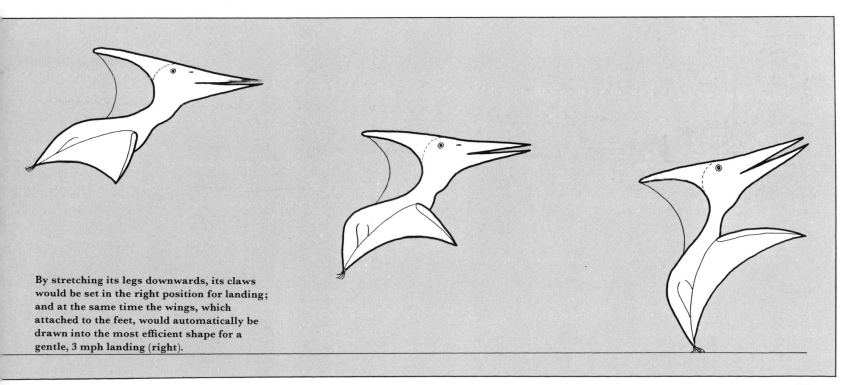

By stretching its legs downwards, its claws would be set in the right position for landing; and at the same time the wings, which attached to the feet, would automatically be drawn into the most efficient shape for a gentle, 3 mph landing (right).

Vulture-like, a flock of *Quetzalcoatlus* gather round the corpse of a sauropod. With their 50-foot wing-span, the creatures would have been able to float,

albatross-like, over immense tracts of territory in search of carrion which they could probe with their eight-foot necks.

air than the root. The air-flow in flapping flight would counteract the effect of the distortion due to the 'yacht-sail' effect. Stein's conclusion: *Pteranodon* would have been most efficient as a flapper, not as a glider.

What then of the supposed upper limits in the weight of muscles? Stein points out that musculature in birds varies between 15 and 35% of the animal's weight, and agrees that if *Pteranodon* was built in proportion it could not have flown at all. But, he adds, bats' muscles comprise only 6 to 10% of the total weight. Can we not assume that *Pteranodon's* muscles were at least that efficient? Moreover bats have a far greater variety of muscles to flap their wings. Stein also suggests that *Pteranodon's* ideal flying speed was slower than previously estimated – no more than 12 mph. On the basis of these calculations and assumptions, take off from a standstill becomes possible, with a wing-beat of one stroke per second. Perhaps in addition the wing was whippy at its tip, a flexibility seen in both bats and pigeons which increases control and efficiency.

Stein also suggests that the crest had an additional function: it may have acted as an anchor for a membrane that stretched down from the skull to the backbone to act as both rudder and a means of controlling the head when the creature was fishing. He calculates that with these lower requirements, *Pteranodon* could have generated 0.1 horsepower but *needed* only 0.07 horsepower. In this analysis *Pteranodon* emerges not as a puzzling anomaly but as a creature of supreme efficiency, 'an animal of long flight endurance, a slow but highly maneuverable flapping species.'

But even with some leeway, would *Pteranodon* not have represented the upper limit of reptilian flying efficiency? Until early 1975 any paleontologist would have answered, unequivocally, yes. But in March of that year a young University of Texas paleontologist, Douglas Lawson, announced a find that made nonsense of any such assertion.

He had been working in the Big Bend National Park on the border of Texas and Mexico, an area of harsh desert, relieved only by a rough cover of scrub and coarse grass. In late Cretaceous times, however, Big Bend was a very different place – swampy and rank with ferns. Knowing that the Park's ancient sediments could be rich in fossils, Lawson had criss-crossed the area on many occasions. One day he spotted some bones partially exposed on the face of a low hill. A little excavation revealed bits of a wing. By 1974 Lawson had identified these and other finds as fragments of a gigantic and previously unknown species of pterosaur.

The Big Bend finds suggested a creature that dwarfed *Pteranodon*. From a 17½-inch humerus – the wing-bone that pivots on the shoulder – Lawson calculated that the animal had a span of around 50 feet. Lawson dramatically dubbed his find *Quetzalcoatlus northropi*, after the Mexican god of the wind and the famous aircraft company. The popular press got around this tongue-twister by calling it simply the 'Texas pterosaur.' For a time Lawson's 'big bird' captured the scientific headlines. The New York Museum of Natural History rushed together a paper-and-wire model that hung high above the floor. The find certainly warranted such attention. Its wing-span was four times that of the largest known flying bird (the wandering albatross, which has been measured at 11 feet ten inches). It seems likely – though such statements are notoriously risky – that the creature was the largest flying animal that has ever existed. It demands a radical rethink of the capabilities of pterosaurs as a whole.

For one thing it had apparently taken the weight-saving talents manifested by *Pteranodon* to even great extremes. Had it been merely a scaled up

Pteranodon, it would have weighed 290 pounds. In fact the huge humerus that Lawson found was so light that it would have been like polystyrene. Although hollow it is strengthened internally by minutely corrugated slats of bone to resist the lengthwise compression applied by the muscles on takeoff.

Indeed it must have been able to take-off. It was an inland dweller. There were no high mountains in Texas at the time; so it could not have relied on cliffs to dive off. Nor could it rely on regular breezes to lift it into the air. The huge bulge on the humerus that Lawson found must clearly have been an attachment for muscles, which equally clearly must have evolved to provide *Quetzalcoatlus* with powered flight.

How it did so without injury to its spindly structure will have to await a full reconstruction. How, for instance, could it beat downwards when standing without hitting its wing-tips on the ground? It is possible that its wings were flexible at their tips. When it took off, the area of wing near the body could have been enough to lift it well clear of the ground in its first flap. The wing-tips, curled upwards out of harm's way, could then have whipped down below the level of the body, providing an extra bit of lift. Once in the air it could have flapped slowly away with wave-like beats of its wings.

It must also have been able to glide extremely efficiently. This would have suited its supposed life style. Its neck bones suggest that it was a scavenger. The best preserved neck vertebrae, which are from *smaller* individuals, are up to 16 inches long. Since there were seven vertebrae in a pterosaur's neck, even a conservative estimate would give the creature a reach of eight or nine feet. On this basis, Lawson concluded that the 'Texas pterosaur' could have been a carrion-eater that used its sinuous neck to probe the carcasses of sauropod dinosaurs.

While the pterosaurs had evolved into the fast moving and efficient creatures that dominated the air from the Triassic period onwards, there had also evolved from some primitive and highly disputed reptilian stock a flying creature of a completely different type: the bird.

The birds are one of the most dramatic life forms ever to have appeared on earth. Their some 9000 species represent one of the five major divisions of vertebrates, along with mammals, reptiles, amphibians and fishes. Their success must depend in large measure on the one thing that marks them as separate – their feathers. How feathers developed and when – and to which creatures birds are most closely related – has been a mystery since the first fossil bird was discovered in 1861. The matter is still one of hot debate.

In 1860 a single fossilized feather was found in the limestone of Solnhofen, Bavaria. The following year a skeleton was found and was entitled *Archaeopteryx lithographica* ('ancient wing from the lithographic limestone'). It created a sensation. Here was a creature that was clearly a bird, in that it possessed feathers; but it was also a reptile in that it had clawed fingers on its wings (as pterosaurs did) and a long bony tail. It was acquired by the District Medical Officer, Dr Karl Häberlain, from the quarry workmen in lieu of medical payments. Häberlain put it up for auction with an asking price of about $3000, allowing collectors to see it before making their bids. For a year Häberlain held out for his asking price. Eventually on Richard Owen's initiative, the Trustees of the British Museum paid up – though they managed to get all the doctor's fossil collection into the bargain – and the slab came to England. There it provided some valuable ammunition for the evolutionists who were delightedly able to reveal a 'missing link,' a species that apparently represented a stage of life transitional between one major life form and another. It was a good investment: *Archaeopteryx* fossils are extremely rare – only five have been found – and such a find today would fetch some $2,000,000.

In 1877 another *Archaeopteryx* came to light. This time, the fossil showed that the creature had teeth. It too was acquired by a Häberlain – Karl's son,

The similarity in size and structure between *Archaeopteryx* (**left**) and *Compsognathus* (**right**), the smallest known dinosaur proper, has long been remarked. Indeed *Archaeopteryx*, usually described as an ancestral bird, can equally well be seen as a feathered dinosaur.

Ernst, who raised the price to $6000. Karl Vogt, Professor of Geology at the University of Geneva, attempted to acquire the trophy for Switzerland. In a speech to Swiss naturalists two years after the discovery, Vogt happened to express some surprise that the Germans appeared to be such cultural barbarians that they would allow a fossil like the *Archaeopteryx* to leave the country. Stung by the insult, a German industrialist beat Ernst Häberlain down to $4000, bought the fossil and sold it at cost to Berlin University.

The archosaurian ancestry of *Archaeopteryx* is not disputed. It is remarkably similar to some of the very lightly built bipedal dinosaurs. Indeed two of the five *Archaeopteryx* specimens had been on display for many years wrongly labeled. A careful examination with side lighting revealed vague shadows of the feathers and allowed them to be properly classified.

A comparison between *Archaeopteryx* and its small bipedal coelurosaurian contemporary, *Compsognathus*, one of the smallest dinosaurs known, reveals similarities. Both were pigeon-sized. Their limbs were very similar (though the *Archaeopteryx* had longer fore-limbs), both had three fingers and four toes, both had long bony tails, both had teeth and both had the abdominal ribs that characterize many dinosaurs.

But what about the feathers? Such extraordinary appendages must have demanded tens of millions of years of evolution. Until recently this was seen as a fundamental division. Bird was bird, and dinosaur was dinosaur. Whatever the similarities, it was widely accepted that any resemblance between *Archaeopteryx* and its dinosaur contemporary was fortuitous. The differences were emphasized, the similarities played down. No modern bird has a tail containing vertebrae; only one – the Amazonian hoatzin – has claws on its wings; *Archaeopteryx* possessed a bird-like wish-bone unknown in dinosaurs. Moreover its hip structure was clearly bird-like and unlike the saurischian pelvis of *Compsognathus*.

Then in 1973 John Ostrom, writing in *Nature*, reasserted the closeness of the similarities. Dinosaurs *have* been unearthed with clavicles or collar-bones, which it is believed, fused together in the ancestors of birds to form wish-bones. He suggested that the apparently backward pointing pubis may have been broken during fossilizing; in life, it could well have been down-turning like that of other carnivorous dinosaurs. He concluded that *Archaeopteryx* must have been derived from an early, or mid-Jurassic theropod.

The significance of that theory, if true, is rather startling: dinosaurs did not become extinct without descendants – their descendants are birds. This theory is far from being accepted, and is indeed merely the latest of several theories that in combination suggest that birds derive from thecodonts, or from saurischians or ornithsischians, or even more remotely, from croco-dilians – a variety of theories that reflect the lack of facts on the origin of birds.

It seems certain, however, that birds have reptilian ancestors of some kind or other. How then to explain feathers? The evolution of the wing has always been a puzzle. A wing, it was once naively assumed, was a device evolved for flight. But how could it evolve? Any creature that attempted flight with an 'evolving' wing would crash-dive to its death. If birds evolved to fly, how to explain the necessarily instantaneous development of the wing? (The spy-cum-dinosaur expert, Baron Nopcsa, had an ingenious suggestion: he proposed that the ancestors of *Archaeopteryx* found that with a set of feathers, long, bouncing strides could with extended arms result in low glides. The trouble with this theory is that long feathers would *not* allow an increase in speed; they would initially offer increased resistance and this would have slowed the creature down.)

This emotive painting is an attempt to re-create the conditions under which *Archaeopteryx* may have become fossilized – a clumsy flyer swept to its death by a high wind in a shallow sea. In fact, *Archaeopteryx* probably could not fly: its bones were too weak to withstand powered flight and its feathers were too loosely attached to provide much support. It is possible wings evolved as a net to snare insects for food.

One way out of this dilemma is to avoid the question, and assume that feathers did not evolve for flight. They could, perhaps, have evolved for insulation, a second response to the evolutionary pressures that in pterosaurs produced fur. It is possible to see the ancestors of *Archaeopteryx* as fast-moving, small dinosaurs, with a high metabolic rate and therefore qualifying as hot-blooded adapted to a colder climate, well insulated by early versions of feathers. Since these early birds could almost certainly climb trees, it requires no great leap of the imagination to see them as evolving an ability to parachute with their feathers as *Longisquama* had done. From there the evolutionary path is open to gliding flight and finally to powered flight which appeared as 'an evolutionary afterthought.'

The strongest argument that feathers were insulation comes from the near-certainty that *Archaeopteryx* could not have actually used them to fly. It lacked a solid breastbone, which provides the main attachment area for the wing muscles in flying birds and any solid crests on the upper arm to which flight muscles would have attached. The shoulder joint is typically dinosaurian: the socket points downwards and the creature would have had difficulty raising its arms high enough to flap effectively. Though slight in dinosaurian terms, it would have been heavily built for a bird and would have needed a tremendous bulk of muscle to get off the ground. Studies on the flying requirements of a bird the size of *Archaeopteryx* have shown that its bone might just have been strong enough to support it in gliding flight but that to flap – even if it had the muscle – would have snapped its arm bones.

The arguments for the hot-bloodedness of *Archaeopteryx* are summarized by Ostrom: feathers insulate; only a hot-blooded creature needs to be insulated; therefore hot-bloodedness had already developed in the ancestors to the *Archaeopteryx*. *Archaeopteryx* needed insulation. With feathers – like fur – a layer of air would be trapped next to the skin and act as a temperature buffer.

The need for insulation could explain much about the evolution of feathers. But it may not be a total explanation. John Ostrom has pointed out that the long wing feathers would not have provided much insulation. Nor would they have been much use if *Archaeopteryx* had been mainly a tree-climber; on the contrary, they would have got in the way. Besides they were not fixed to the bone and must have been loosely implanted in the flesh. They would not have provided any support in gliding or parachuting.

Ostrom suggests that being a running predator and needing to be well insulated, *Archaeopteryx* may have used its feathers as a net to surround and trap insects before grasping them with its claws. Perhaps it was this, he suggests, that demanded the high co-ordination necessary for flight.

The essential link between ground dwelling predators and flyers is missing but by Cretaceous times there *were* birds. They were apparently beginning to rival the pterosaurs. Towards the end of the Cretaceous there were 14 known genera of birds. But it was only after the end of the dinosaurs – and the pterosaurs – that the birds came into their own.

To explain the distortion of this *Coelophysis* fossil, it was once suggested that dinosaurs perished en masse from eating poisonous plants.

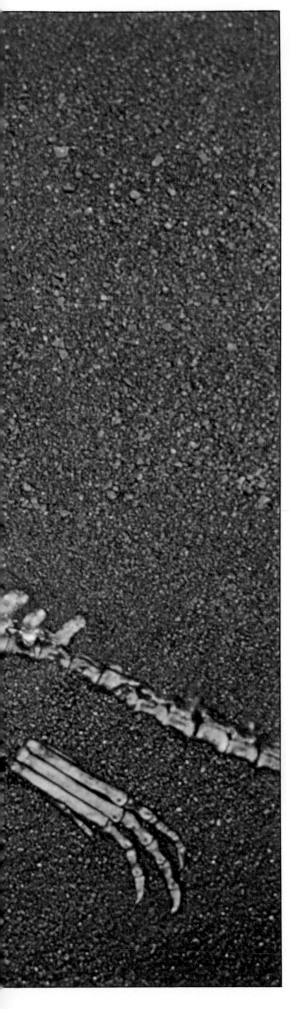

6/The Great Death

Sixty-five million years ago, the dinosaurs vanished. This event, which marks the end of the Cretaceous period, must rank as one of the most startling occurrences in the history of life on earth. After 140 million years of steadily increasing success, the dinosaurs – and many hundreds of other contemporary species on the land, in the air and in the sea – disappeared from the face of the earth. One stratum reveals in its fossil record a wide diversity of creatures, another stratum, just a few million years younger, contains by comparison a mere handful. Somehow almost all large creatures on earth had been obliterated. No wonder this critical period has been called by one German geologist, Johannes Walther, 'the time of the great death.'

Stated in this fashion, the problem seems a simple one: what force could have brought about such a catastrophe? When posed in this way – with the assumption of a rapid catastrophic extermination – the question seems to demand a simple explanation. And explanations there have been in plenty, most of them dramatically straightforward and some of them laughably bizarre. Before we look at the question in depth, consider this checklist of suggested explanations for the death of the dinosaurs:

- climatic change: the world, warm and muggy for so long, began to dry out and get even hotter so that the dinosaurs got roasted out of existence. Alternatively the climate became colder and they froze to death.
- they became so successful that they ate up all their food and died of starvation.
- their food became poisoned.
- they were killed by disease, or newly evolved parasites. (Such suggestions keep reappearing. In April 1977 a Russian scientist, V Eliseyev, suggested that the dinosaurs died of rickets. The heavy Cretaceous rains, he said, leached lime from the soil, which meant that plants and animals became calcium deficient. The dinosaurs' bones simply wasted away).

- the dinosaurs became so heavy that their bodies simply refused to work. They slipped their discs too frequently to survive.
- the atmosphere changed. Volcanoes, meteorites, or comets poisoned the earth.
- the dinosaur eggs were all stolen by agile, nimble and intelligent mammals.
- the dinosaurs died of 'racial old age' – a concept suggesting that species can be treated as individuals and that after a time they simply succumb to senescence.
- the carnivorous dinosaurs ate all the herbivorous dinosaurs and then died of hunger themselves.
- a star exploded nearby in the galaxy and doused the earth in a lethal dose of radiation.
- the gravity of a passing star pulled the earth in two, thus creating the moon; the resulting catastrophic earthquakes and tidal waves wiped out the dinosaurs.
- geological changes brought droughts and floods with which the dinosaurs could not cope.
- they could not stand to live any more and died of depression, or, as one scientist described it, 'paleo-*Weltschmerz*.'
- they could not cope with the chemistry of the newly-evolved flowering plants and died of constipation.
- newly-evolved insects, living off the flowering plants, ate them out of existence.

In Walt Disney's *Fantasia*, **the dinosaurs lumber to their death under a pitiless desert sun. In this haunting sequence, the great beasts perish in a fruitless search for vanishing water holes. In fact, the climate at the end of the Age of Reptiles became cooler, not hotter.**

However much fun such suggestions are, they do not help us to understand the extinction. The inadequacies of most of these explanations becomes clear if the problem is restated in terms that conform a little more to the known facts. It is then possible to ask what patterns can be devised to fit the findings. Often the search for a pattern that fits involves a search for the right questions. Only then can the right answers be found. There *is*, at last, the basis of a theory, which scientists should be able to work out over the next few years – one that involves the great concept of continental drift.

What exactly did vanish at the end of the Cretaceous? The dinosaurs themselves went: the giant sauropods, the herds of horned dinosaurs, the iguanodons, the hadrosaurs, the tyrannosaurs, the ankylosaurs – amounting to several hundred species in all. Many other reptilian forms also vanished with them: pterosaurs – including of course the last of the flying giants, the *Quetzalcoatlus* – ichthyosaurs, plesiosaurs and mosasaurs. Toothed birds became extinct; so too did ammonites, shelled molluscs that were coiled into flat spirals rather like a modern nautilus; many groups of sea-snail and other whole groups of squid-like and cuttle-fish-like sea creatures called belemnites.

But one of the most telling features about the so-called Cretaceous-Tertiary boundary – besides the disappearance of the dinosaurs – is the change in microscopic life-forms in the sea. Of these, the most significant for our purposes are the foraminifera, tiny, shelled creatures that range in size from the microscopic up to about two inches across. They are an important constituent in plankton, those minute life-forms, both plant and animal, that drift by the countless billion in the sea, turning it into an organic soup on which almost all marine life is ultimately dependent. From the surface, the minute shells of the hundreds of species of foraminifera rain down continuously on the bottom where they form a major part of the so-called 'globigerina ooze' which covers about 30% of the ocean floor. Their fossil record is extraordinary. Their shells – or tests – are found in marine strata over two-thirds of the world's existing land areas and they thus serve as a good indication of the extent of ancient seas. There is, for instance, a 200-foot stratum of foraminifera at the 22,000-foot level on Mount Everest. During the Cretaceous when the sea-level was high, foraminifera were widely distributed across North America and Europe. The White Cliffs of Dover were laid down at this time.

At the end of the Cretaceous, countless existing species of foraminifera vanished from the fossil record to be replaced by species of a totally different type. Many of the Cretaceous species were unusually large, yet those that marked the beginning of the Tertiary were singularly small. On this evidence a delegate at the International Geological Congress in 1960 concluded that at the end of the Cretaceous there was a major regression of the sea and a drastic cooling of the oceans. The death of the dinosaurs coincided with the onset of a colder climate.

The evidence for such a change is strong too from the fossil record of pollen grains, which are the toughest part of plants and leave a record in the rock of the plant life of each period. In eastern Montana, fossil pollen reveals that half of all late Cretaceous plants were flowering plants. Early in the Tertiary, the proportion had dropped to less than one-third and the conifers, which can tolerate colder conditions, had increased their hold.

How long did such changes take? The destruction of foraminifera could have been very rapid. Estimates have varied from a few days to a million years. Trees, of course, spread relatively slowly: it would take several hundred generations for a forest community to be replaced in a changing climate.

A herd of hadrosaurs – some of the last, yet also some of the most successful dinosaurs – browse on late Cretaceous vegetation. One member of the herd

sniffs the breeze to identify a new smell – another source of food, perhaps, or a prowling predator.

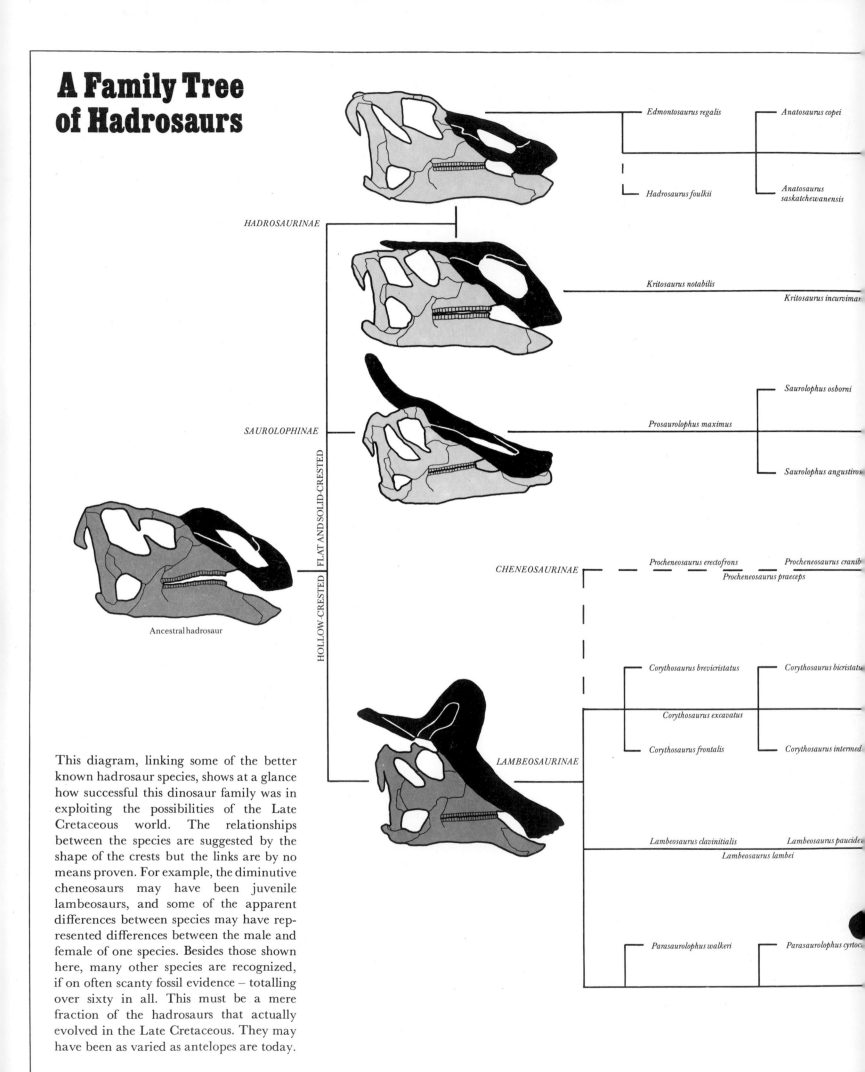

A Family Tree of Hadrosaurs

HADROSAURINAE

SAUROLOPHINAE

Ancestral hadrosaur

HOLLOW-CRESTED   FLAT AND SOLID-CRESTED

CHENEOSAURINAE

LAMBEOSAURINAE

Edmontosaurus regalis

Hadrosaurus foulkii

Anatosaurus copei

Anatosaurus saskatchewanensis

Kritosaurus notabilis

Kritosaurus incurvimar

Saurolophus osborni

Prosaurolophus maximus

Saurolophus angustiros

Procheneosaurus erectofrons

Procheneosaurus cranib

Procheneosaurus praeceps

Corythosaurus brevicristatus

Corythosaurus bicristatu

Corythosaurus excavatus

Corythosaurus frontalis

Corythosaurus intermed

Lambeosaurus clavinitialis

Lambeosaurus paucide

Lambeosaurus lambei

Parasaurolophus walkeri

Parasaurolophus cyrtoc

This diagram, linking some of the better known hadrosaur species, shows at a glance how successful this dinosaur family was in exploiting the possibilities of the Late Cretaceous world. The relationships between the species are suggested by the shape of the crests but the links are by no means proven. For example, the diminutive cheneosaurs may have been juvenile lambeosaurs, and some of the apparent differences between species may have represented differences between the male and female of one species. Besides those shown here, many other species are recognized, if on often scanty fossil evidence – totalling over sixty in all. This must be a mere fraction of the hadrosaurs that actually evolved in the Late Cretaceous. They may have been as varied as antelopes are today.

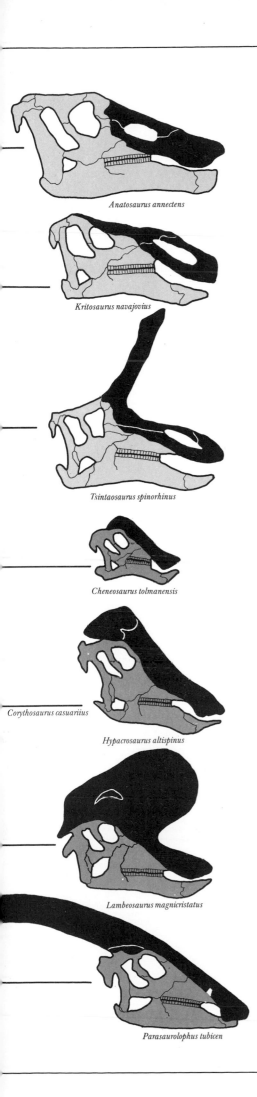

Anatosaurus annectens

Kritosaurus navajovius

Tsintaosaurus spinorhinus

Cheneosaurus tolmanensis

Corythosaurus casuariius

Hypacrosaurus altispinus

Lambeosaurus magnicristatus

Parasaurolophus tubicen

The fossil record of dinosaurs also indicates that their end was not immediate. In the penultimate Cretaceous bed of the American west, 16 genera of horn dinosaurs have been found, while in the last stratum there were only seven genera represented. The armored dinosaurs show a similar reduction, from 19 to six genera, and the duck-billed forms from 29 to seven. In this perspective the final extinction at the end of the Cretaceous should be seen as the culmination of a steady process that went on over a period of several million years.

What survived the change? Firstly the mammals, which were already beginning to diversify. At the end of the Cretaceous the largest mammals, already divided into placentals (whose young are born at an advanced stage of development) and marsupials (whose young are raised in pouches) were probably the size of a cat. The birds survived, and then, after the extinction of the dinosaurs, exploded into a wide variety of types. The fishes came through largely unscathed. But most puzzling of all, a few reptilian types also survived – turtles, crocodiles, lizards, snakes (which had evolved only a short time before) and the peculiar tuatara of New Zealand, the sole surviving member of an obscure and pre-dinosaurian group of reptiles.

There are two other factors that should be emphasized: throughout the Cretaceous, sea-levels were high, as the evidence of foraminifera deposits shows. Huge deposits of chalk were laid down by seas that spread across Central Europe, North Africa and the mid-west of the United States. But at the end of the Cretaceous, the seas retreated, exposing areas that had been previously covered. Secondly by the end of the Cretaceous the continents were almost completely split up. Eurasia, Africa, India, Antarctica, still joined to Australia and the Americas (which were linked only by a narrow isthmus, as now) were all separate continental islands.

What patterns can be imposed on these facts that make sense of them?

Let us look first at some of the more widely discussed theories in detail and examine the objections to them: almost all of them are either too limited, in that they should really apply only to individual species, or too general, in that they do not account for the selectivity of the great death.

Take, for instance, the suggestion that disease was responsible for the extinction of the dinosaurs. There are indeed virulent diseases that have swept through animal and human populations – rabies, rinderpest, anthrax, myxomatosis, the Black Death. There are two remarkable things about such plagues: one is that they do not in fact wipe out complete species, however virulent they are. A small percentage of individuals – either through immunity or luck – escapes to rebuild the population. Myxomatosis was introduced into Australia to control the plague of rabbits; but although it can wipe out 90% of a population in a fairly short space of time, it is remarkable how little lasting impact such a catastrophe has. Within a few years – a mere eye-blink of geological time which would never be recorded in the fossil record – the population balance is restored (in Australia, myxomatosis is now 30% fatal) and the more normal limits imposed by food supply and natural predators prevail once again. Such is the case with other equivalent catastrophes. Lemmings, driven every few years to run themselves into the sea in a frantic search for food, rebuild their depleted populations rapidly.

Secondly very few plagues affect several species equally. Bubonic plague killed one-third of the human population of Europe in the fourteenth century but it had no impact at all on the rats that carried the fleas that carried the disease. There are diseases that affect closely related species but no disease is known that could affect a whole class – all mammals, or all birds –

simultaneously. Moreover even if there were such a disease, why would it leave some of the group of creatures completely unharmed? And why should the disease spread to the seas? And how, given the position of the continents, could such a disease have spread from one continental land-mass to another?

One once-popular idea was that of racial senility. It was claimed that whole races of creatures could grow old, just as individuals grew old, until they finally expired through old age. Evidence of senility was seen in the apparent 'extremes' of later dinosaurian evolution – the odd bony frills of *Triceratops*, the plumes of some hadrosaurs, the thick skulls of the dome-headed dinosaurs.

This argument, though initially appealing, does not withstand analysis. Since nothing physical passes from one generation to the next – genetic information is duplicated afresh – what exactly would 'age'? Would such aging apply to one species – in which case, is one to assume that a variety of species became old simultaneously by pure coincidence? Or does aging apply to groups of related species? Either way, why should some species apparently survive unscathed for many millions of years when other species succumb after a shorter life span? Finally – and most conclusively – why should a species, or a group of species be treated as an individual entity? Species evolve continuously, with varieties leading to new species. Often they do not die out at all: they change into something else.

Such philosophical problems in the theory lead back to the supposed evidence for racial old age: the 'extremes' of adaptation displayed by late Cretaceous dinosaurs. A second look at these 'extremes' shows that the evidence for senility lies in the mind of the observer, not in the creatures themselves. Even the most bizarre adaptations evolved for a particular purpose and are there because they conferred some benefit on an individual, which survived at least long enough to breed.

Far from indicating senility, the range of adaptations in the later dinosaurs seems to display an *increasing*, not decreasing evolutionary vigor. They filled in their own ways niches equivalent to those now occupied by lions, ostriches, elephants, buffalo and crocodiles. Among the last dinosaurs were some of the most impressive. Hadrosaurs could have had senses as delicate as our own – stereoscopic vision, an opposable thumb and extraordinary co-ordination.

The wide variety of dinosaurs suggests a possible science fiction scenario: if the history of the earth had turned out differently, the Cretaceous might have been the beginning of a great new dinosaurian evolutionary chapter, rather than the end of one. What might not have evolved from such creatures, which had some of the characteristics of the apes and monkeys that emerged some 40 million years later? Perhaps in some different dimension of time, we can imagine intelligent dinosaurs, with another 65 million years of evolution behind them, observing the fossil record and wondering why those tiny, furry creatures, the mammals, never evolved into species of any significance.

In the search for causes to explain dinosaur extinction, scientists have naturally concentrated on those elements in the late Cretaceous that were new and to which the dinosaurs might not have been able to adapt. One such novelty was the emergence of the flowering plants which came into existence about 120 million years ago. It has been seen as significant that the extinction of the dinosaurs followed. Tony Swain of the Royal Botanic Gardens in Kew, has done a detailed analysis of the differences in the possible biochemical effects of the non-flowering plants (like ferns and conifers) and the flowering plants. The non-flowering plants contained tannins with which the herbivorous dinosaurs had coped well enough for tens of millions of years. The

The impact that dinosaurs have had on the public has largely been a result of the imagination of scientists and artists. The illustrations in this book offer numerous examples. But writers have also made their contribution. One of the best known 'portraits' of a dinosaur in action appears in Sir Arthur Conan Doyle's *The Lost World*, in which explorers in South America discover an isolated plateau where species long extinct elsewhere have survived. In this extract, the hero, Ed Malone, a journalist is pursued by a *Tyrannosaurus*. He escapes, somewhat miraculously, by falling into a dinosaur trap dug by the human inhabitants of the plateau. This description, written in 1912, reflects the then popular – but already discredited – view that bipedal dinosaurs hopped like kangaroos. In addition, the beast is portrayed with powerful forearms; they were in fact residual.

' . . . I was plodding up the slope when my mind was brought back to my own position by a strange noise behind me. It was something between a snore and a growl, low, deep, and exceedingly menacing. Some strange creature was evidently near me, but nothing could be seen, so I hastened more rapidly upon my way. I had traversed half a mile or so when suddenly the sound was repeated, still behind me, but louder and more menacing than before. My heart stood still within me as it flashed across me that the beast, whatever it was,

flowering plants contained a new sort of substance, the alkaloids, most of which produce harmful physiological changes in men and animals. Examples of alkaloids are morphine, quinine, nicotine and strychnine. Almost a thousand alkaloids are known, most of them restricted to particular groups of plants and most toxic in some degree (although about 20 are used in carefully controlled amounts for medicinal purposes). The effects are usually remarkably specific – raising blood pressure, stimulating the respiratory system, affecting the mind and behavior (as mescalin does), producing paralysis (curare, the arrow poison of the South American Indians).

Swain found that reptiles were less aware of such poisons than mammals. For instance, tortoises ate 40 times as much of an alkaloidal plant than mammals before becoming sensitized and cutting down their intake. He concluded that, since both tortoises and dinosaurs are reptiles, the dinosaurs were 'unable to detect [such compounds] in low enough concentration to be harmless [and] may well have eaten enough to suffer severe physiological disturbance and even death.' The implication is that once the herbivores vanished, the carnivores followed.

It is a nice idea but it raises difficulties. In the first place it is unfair to

Pursued by a Tyrannosaur

must surely be after *me*. My skin grew cold and my hair rose at the thought. That these monsters should tear each other to pieces was a part of the strange struggle for existence, but that they should turn upon modern man, that they should deliberately track and hunt down the predominant human, was a staggering and fearsome thought. . . . With my knees shaking beneath me, I stood and glared with starting eyes down the moonlit path which lay behind me. All was quiet as in a dream landscape. Silver clearings and the black patches of the bushes – nothing else could I see. Then from out of the silence, imminent and threatening, there came once more that low, throaty croaking, far louder and closer than before. There could no longer be a doubt. Something was on my trail, and was closing in upon me every minute.

I stood like a man paralysed, still staring at the ground which I had traversed. Then suddenly I saw it. There was movement among the bushes at the far end of the clearing which I had just traversed. A great dark shadow disengaged itself and hopped out into the clear moonlight. I say "hopped" advisedly, for the beast moved like a kangaroo, springing along in an erect position upon its powerful hind-legs, while its front ones were held bent in front of it. It was of enormous size and power, like an erect elephant, but its movements, in spite of its bulk, were exceedingly alert. For a moment, as I saw its shape, I hoped that

it was an iguanodon, which I knew to be harmless, but, ignorant as I was, I soon saw that this was a very different creature. Instead of the gentle, deer-shaped head of the great three-toed leaf-eater, this beast had a broad, squat, toad-like face like that which had alarmed us in our camp. His ferocious cry and the horrible energy of his pursuit both assured me that this was surely one of the great flesh-eating dinosaurs, the most terrible beasts which have ever walked this earth. As the huge brute loped along it dropped forward upon its fore-paws and brought its nose to the ground every twenty yards or so. It was smelling out my trail. . . .

Even now when I think of that nightmare the sweat breaks out upon my brow. What could I do? My useless fowling-piece was in my hand. What help could I get from that? I looked desperately round for some rock or tree, but I was in a bushy jungle with nothing higher than a sapling within sight, while I knew that the creature behind me could tear down an ordinary tree as though it were a reed. My only possible chance lay in flight. I could not move swiftly over the rough, broken ground, but as I looked round me in despair I saw a well-marked, hard-beaten path which ran across in front of me. We had seen several of the sort, the runs of various wild beasts, during our expeditions. Along this I could perhaps hold my own, for I was a fast runner, and in excellent con-

dition. Flinging away my useless gun, I set myself to do such a half mile as I have never done before or since. My limbs ached, my chest heaved, I felt that my throat would burst for want of air, and yet with that horror behind me I ran and I ran and ran. At last I paused, hardly able to move. For a moment I thought that I had thrown him off. The path lay still behind me. And then suddenly, with a crashing and a rending, a thudding of giant feet and a panting of monster lungs, the beast was upon me once more. He was at my very heels. I was lost.

Madman that I was to linger so long before I fled! Up to then he had hunted by scent, and his movement was slow. But he had actually seen me as I started to run. From then onwards he had hunted by sight, for the path showed him where I had gone. Now, as he came round the curve, he was springing in great bounds. The moonlight shone upon his huge, projecting eyes, the rows of enormous teeth in his open mouth, and the gleaming fringe of claws upon his short, powerful forearms. With a scream of terror I turned and rushed wildly down the path. Behind me the thick, gasping breathing of the creature sounded louder and louder. His heavy footfall was beside me. Every instant I expected to feel his grip upon my back. And then suddenly there came a crash – I was falling through space, and everything beyond was darkness and rest.'

compare tortoises with dinosaurs whose physiology was possibly more equivalent to that of modern mammals than modern reptiles. Again there is the problem of selectivity: fish-eating pterosaurs and plesiosaurs should not have been affected but were. Turtles and tortoises should have been but were not.

The most serious objection however, is one of chronology: the dinosaurs survived for some 50 million years after the emergence of the flowering plants. It looks strongly as if the argument should be stood on its head and that it was the development of the flowering plants that allowed the dinosaurs to diversify in the way that they did. The bird-hipped dinosaurs, which had only a moderate success in Jurassic times, increased five-fold in the late Cretaceous times. Two new large groups – the armored and the horned types – evolved. The hadrosaurs produced whole batteries of teeth to cope with the new source of food.

One argument that might seem to support death by poisoning is the peculiar distorted pose in which some skeletons are found. A number of those with long necks have, in death or fossilization, been contorted so that the neck seems to have been thrown over the back. One explanation for these contortions is that they were the result of death throes brought on by strychnine poisoning, which does indeed induce muscular spasms before death. However such distortions are not limited to dinosaurs, nor are they limited to the Cretaceous; it seems likely that desiccation of the neck tendons immediately after death causes the contortion before fossilization occurs.

Another theory is that the dinosaurs were eaten out of house and home by the arrival of the butterflies and moths, with their voracious plant-eating larvae – the caterpillars. It was the caterpillars, it has been suggested, that defoliated the world, hence depriving the herbivores of their food and consequently starving the carnivores as well. One almost insuperable obstacle to this theory is that the oldest known caterpillar fossils are from the Tertiary, long after the extinction of the dinosaurs. But let us suppose – the fossil record being incomplete – that there were caterpillars in the Cretaceous. Caterpillars nowadays are controlled by the birds which feed upon them. It is pretty certain that had a new food source like caterpillars evolved, the birds themselves would have evolved rapidly to take advantage of them. Moreover if there were too few birds, why did not the dinosaurs themselves develop a liking for caterpillars?

Perhaps the most startling and one of the most compelling of the suggested explanations is that of a cosmic catastrophe – the type of event that would rival, in drama, the great extinction. One such catastrophe might have been a stellar explosion – a nova or supernova – occurring close enough to the earth to shower it with lethal cosmic radiation.

A nova ('new star') is a star that has exploded (a fate that may be a normal part of the evolution of all stars). A nova outburst may be from a hundred times to a million times brighter than the original star and the change characteristically takes place in just a few days. A supernova is an explosion that reaches many times that brightness. The total energy emitted by a nova may equal the radiation from the sun over 10,000 years but the total radiation emitted in a few days by a supernova may equal the energy radiated by the sun during 1000 million years. Seen from earth one supernova in a distant galaxy – one star in perhaps 100 million – may outshine all its neighbors. On average there is about one supernova per galaxy every 300 years. There have been five in our Milky Way during

This fast expanding cloud of gas is the remnant of a supernova – the Crab Nebula – which appeared in 1054 A.D. Although the Crab is 5000 light years away, for a time it outshone the planet Venus. If such an explosion occurred near our own solar system – within 20 light years – it would blanket the earth in a possibly lethal dose of radiation. A local supernova has been suggested as the factor – or a contributing factor – in the extinction of the dinosaurs but the theory is hard to prove: after 65 million years of expansion, its gaseous remnants would be so scattered as to be almost undetectable.

the last 1000 years, most notably, perhaps, that observed by Chinese astronomers in 1054. The remnant of this explosion, known as the Crab Nebula, is a cloud of gas expanding at the rate of several hundred miles per second.

It is likely that several times in its history the earth has been bombarded by radiation from a nearby supernova, one that is within about 20 light years of the earth. It has been estimated that a local supernova in our own galaxy will occur once in a hundred years. Whenever this occurred, the radiation level at the top of the atmosphere would shoot up about 100,000-fold. The effects of such an explosion on life on earth might be catastrophic. In particular the radiation would, by a rapid chemical process, destroy the ozone layer, which mops up almost all of the harmful short-wave radiation from the sun. Such destruction of the ozone layer would expose the earth's surface to the sun's lethal ultra-violet rays. Cosmic ray intensity might increase a 100-fold and, since about one-third of the radio-activity of the earth's surface is the result of cosmic radiation, radio activity would go up 30-fold. If such an event occurred now, we might expect a dramatic rise in skin cancer, an increase in the mutation rate and extreme climatic changes (though whether we would fry or freeze is open to some dispute). If a local supernova occurred at the end of the Cretaceous, the dinosaurs would – according to this argument – have been subjected to rapid, unendurable assaults on their bodies and habitats.

There are a number of objections to this dramatic and appealing theory. They relate to the two suggested effects: an increase in radiation and a change of climate.

To suggest radiation as the agent of destruction again involves the problem of selectivity. Given the similarity between the small, fast dinosaurs and birds, why should one have been exterminated and the other survive? In addition given the fact that a few inches of water can cut radiation even at that high level to practically nothing, how is it that some large marine creatures of reptilian origin vanished, while the fishes remained unaffected? It is possible to assume that mammals, being small, might have burrowed out of the way of intense solar radiation but it is a little hard to accept that *all* Cretaceous species were burrowers and that *all* would have remained underground fortuitously for the several days or weeks that it took to deliver a lethal dose of radiation.

But a supernova might also have climatic effects, the implications of which have been analyzed by Dale Russell of the National Museum of Natural Sciences in Ottawa and Wallace Tucker of American Science and Engineering in Boston. They argue that a heavy dose of radiation in the upper atmospheric layers would draw lower, moister air upwards, where it would form ice crystals that would reflect the sun's rays, causing a dramatic drop in temperature all over the world. It was the cold, they argue, and not the radiation that caused the extinctions.

Yet this theory too, suggests an instant catastrophe, a fact that is in conflict with the progressive diminution of dinosaur fossils through the strata of the late Cretaceous period.

Nevertheless the suggestion of a colder climate, extended over a long period of time, is worth closer examination. Suppose we simply postulate a colder climate, without at first seeking an explanation. Could a new ice-age have spelt the end of the dinosaurs?

Perhaps: the dinosaurs emerged into an equitable and warm climate at the end of the Triassic. They had an efficient body chemistry that was comparable to that of a mammal and they certainly had no problem in dissipating the heat that they generated. What the dinosaurs did not have, and did not need, was any means of insulation. They did not have to evolve adaptations to keep warm; their high metabolism and huge bulk, in combination with a warm climate, were sufficient to ensure a stable, high temperature. Though the pterosaurs, lacking bulk, developed a furry covering, the dinosaurs themselves were naked. In a uniform, world-wide cold snap, they would have no way to preserve their heat. True, the larger adults could have done so over a period of perhaps several weeks because their immense size preserved heat but their offspring and the smaller species would have frozen as easily as plucked chickens in an ice-box.

On the other hand there is no evidence for a uniform cold snap over the whole world. There was still an equator. Tropical forests diminished but they did not disappear. The Cretaceous rain-forests of Borneo and the Amazon were very like today's forests. Though the dinosaurs might have been exterminated from many regions by cold, there is no apparent reason why they should not have survived in isolated pockets. After all there are many relict communities of creatures scattered about the world, survivors from a former age, whose niche has remained little touched. Why did no herbivores survive on the edges of the Amazon Basin, along with the carnivores that preyed on them? Why should the crocodiles which are even more sluggish and, apparently, more susceptible to cold, survive? No: climate, which certainly could have played some part in the great death, is not in itself a sufficient explanation.

Is Nessie a Plesiosaur?

Since the first dramatic photograph of a supposed Loch Ness monster, taken in 1934, the evidence that there are as yet unidentified creatures in the loch has mounted dramatically. 'Sightings' have risen into the hundreds. Sonar tracings, cine films, and underwater photographs have added additional evidence. It is not conclusive because the photographs – especially those taken in the thick, peaty water – are indistinct. Nevertheless the weight of evidence is impressive. Roy

Mackal, in his detailed study *The Monsters of Loch Ness*, concludes 'that a population of moderate sized, piscivorous, aquatic animals is inhabiting Loch Ness.'

The evidence suggests that the creatures – of which there must be enough to form a breeding community – can swim at up to 10 mph, grow up to 25 feet long, and live mainly in the depths, but can also (though rarely) venture on to land. They have small heads, bulbous bodies and tails. The few land sightings suggest that the creatures also have front flippers. Sightings in the water indicate the existence of at least two 'humps.'

It is theoretically possible for a community of animals to live in Loch Ness.

They would have space enough – the loch is 900 feet deep in places – and the loch's immense quantities of salmon would make an ideal food supply. But what type of creature could 'Nessie' be?

One theory is that the monster is a plesiosaur. Plesiosaurs were roughly the right shape, could swim fast and fed on fish. Moreover, an underwater picture of a 'flipper' taken in 1972 by Robert Rines closely resembles that of a plesiosaur.

There are however three major objections to the suggestion. Plesiosaurs were air breathing, and if there were a whole community of the creatures in Loch Ness, the surface would be broken several times an hour as the animals rose to breathe.

Secondly, the temperature of the water is a fairly constant 42° – too cold for any known reptile. Thirdly, 10,000 years ago Loch Ness, like the rest of northern Europe, was under several hundred yards of ice. The creatures must therefore have come into Loch Ness after the retreat of the ice cap. The idea that plesiosaurs could have unaccountably survived for 65 million years, entered Loch Ness, after the end of the Ice Age and then died out elsewhere, stretches the scientific credulity beyond breaking point.

Mackal does suggest a creature that largely conforms to the available evidence – an amphibian, like that shown in silhouette here.

Plesiosaurs had the head, neck, body and flippers that fit many Nessie 'sightings.'

This is perhaps the best known of all Loch Ness photos. It was taken in April 1934 by R K Wilson, a London surgeon. It appears to show an animal's head rising out of the water, some 200 to 300 yards from shore. It is, perhaps, the strongest evidence to support the hypothesis that Nessie is a plesiosaur. Many other explanations have been offered: that it shows an otter, for instance, or a diving bird. Dr Wilson said the creature was too large to be either.

These silhouettes represent hypothetical male and female amphibians devised by Roy Mackal to fit a high proportion of the evidence for the existence of an unknown creature in Loch Ness.

There is, however, the beginning of an answer, as Bob Bakker has written in a paper entitled *Tetrapod Mass Extinctions*. He points out in conversation that the theory does not depend on new information. 'What we need,' he says, 'is a conceptual revolution. We've had the data for years.'

He starts with the assumption that we should not be looking for new and dramatic explanations for the Cretaceous extinction. Extinctions are as much a pattern of life as the evolution of new species. The two processes go hand in hand, and any change – of which there have been many in the history of the earth – brings about a concentration of extinctions that may look dramatic in the fossil record but, in fact, merely reflect an intensification of the natural order of events.

Secondly he points out that in the great death at the end of the Cretaceous the really striking thing is not the type of creature that was eradicated but its size. Generally anything over about 22 pounds vanished. Anything weighing less than that survived. These weight limits happen to exclude all the mammals and include all the dinosaurs. Had there been a mammal of 22 pounds or more, it too would have vanished. Those reptiles that survived were all under 22 pounds, with the exception of crocodiles and turtles, which form a special case.

Thirdly Bakker argues that animals cannot be considered *in vacuo*. They live in environments; we should rephrase our question by asking not why the dinosaurs vanished but why their habitats vanished.

And fourthly as an extension of this point, he argues that extinctions can be seen in two ways. One may ask: 'Why did the creatures die out?' which is the

The Horns and Frills of Reptilian Rhinos

Like the hadrosaurs, the ceratopsians also proved remarkably successful in Late Cretaceous times. The suggestion that the dinosaurs became extinct simply because they were unable to adapt to changing conditions cannot stand up in the face of the evidence of their success.

The horned and frilled rhinoceros-like creatures evolved from the six-foot, one-and-a-half-ton *Protoceratops* into many different kinds (of which the major ones are listed here). They lived mainly in what is now North America. As with many families, the later species tended to be larger. Some species had a single horn, others developed two additional horns over the eyes. There was also wide variety in the shape of the bony frills that extended backwards from the neck. All ceratopsians, however, had horny beaks tipping a narrow sharp-toothed jaw to cut through the tough, palm-like plants on which they lived.

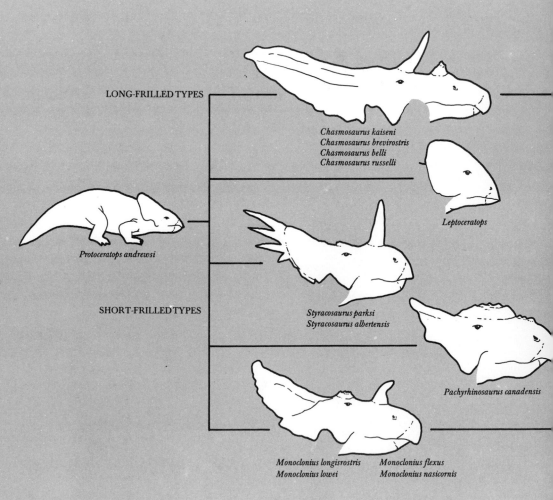

LONG-FRILLED TYPES

Chasmosaurus kaiseni
Chasmosaurus brevirostris
Chasmosaurus belli
Chasmosaurus russelli

Leptoceratops

Protoceratops andrewsi

SHORT-FRILLED TYPES

Styracosaurus parksi
Styracosaurus albertensis

Pachyrhinosaurus canadensis

Monoclonius longisrostris   *Monoclonius flexus*
Monoclonius lowei   *Monoclonius nasicornis*

usual way of looking at the problem; or – since extinctions are as much a feature of life as the evolution of new species – one can rephrase the question and ask: why did no new species emerge to replace those that would have gone extinct anyway? To answer this, he believes that the most fruitful approach is to seek patterns underlying all extinctions.

In his search for an explanation Bakker began to look at the patterns of extinction from Permian times right through to the end of the Cretaceous. Seen in this context the death of the dinosaurs seems somewhat less dramatic. Bakker identifies several 'extinction events' in the 200 or so million years from the end of the Permian to the end of the Cretaceous.

It is, he points out, a good time to study such events, because for much of the time the world was one single land-mass. Even right at the end of the Cretaceous, when Pangaea had almost broken up, there were still narrow land-bridges between some of the major continental areas and the various dinosaurian communities do not show the extraordinary variety that is exhibited by life-forms in the world today. The differences are one of quantity rather than quality. For instance South America had a few hadrosaurs but many sauropods, whereas western North America had lots of ceratopsians and very few sauropods.

Next he summarizes what is in effect a theory of the ecological forces behind the evolutionary process. He recalls that most fossils are found in the flood-plain areas on the edges of continental land-masses. But these habitats are limited, they do not reflect the variety of species that actually existed on the continent at any one time. Nor do they act as a major evolutionary stimulus

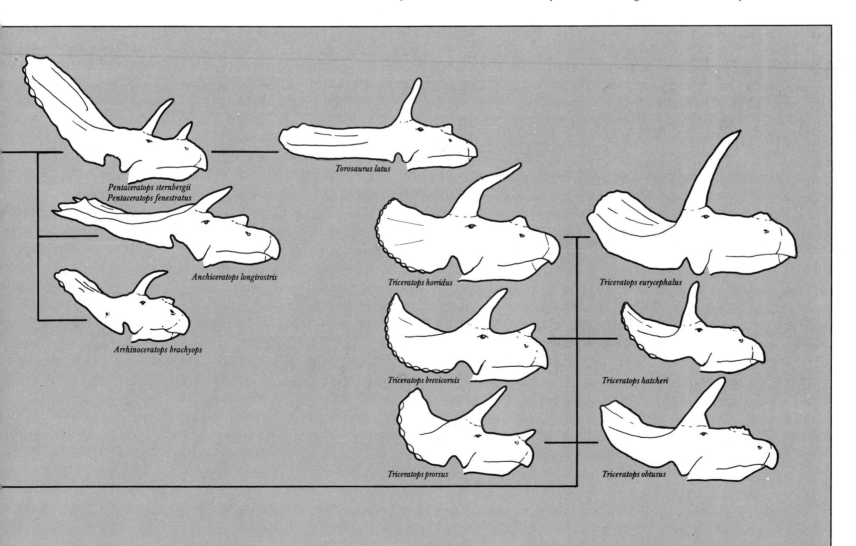

The Descendants

The only true descendants of the dinosaurs are the birds. Of the reptilian contempories of the dinosaurs, only five groups survived the great death at the end of the Cretaceous. They are all still with us. Perhaps the closest to the dinosaurs themselves are the crocodiles, which are the only surviving archosaurs, the group to which dinosaurs also belonged. In fact, the Nile crocodile or the American alligator represent types that have changed remarkably little in the last 200 million years. Their continued success would seem assured, but for the challenge of man himself. Modern tortoises and turtles trace their ancestory back as far as the crocodiles do. The lizards go back almost as far, though the snakes, their close relatives, evolved only in the Late Cretaceous. Perhaps the oddest survivor is the tuatara of New Zealand, which is the single direct descendant of an otherwise extinct branch of the main reptilian stem, the rhynchocephalia.

TUATARA

AMERICAN ALLIGATOR

GREEN TURTLE

SOUTH AFRICAN GECKO

INDIAN PYTHON

for the emergence of new species. Species develop in the continental interiors, where the variety of habitats – plains, forests, rivers, mountains, deserts – provide a wider variety of possible niches. They also form the large natural barriers that keep new varieties of old species separated until they have evolved enough to count as a new species. From the interior new species filter down into the lowlands. Assuming therefore that most of the animals that appear in the fossil record evolved in the continental interior, the question we should ask in order to seek an explanation of the great death is: *why did species stop evolving in the continental interiors?*

In his search for an answer Bakker returns to the dynasties of animal communities and the 'extinction events' that can be identified from the Permian to the Cretaceous. In all these communities there is, Bakker argues, a pattern: they begin with a low diversity of species, particularly of the large herbivores. Diversity steadily increases, with a consequent increase in the number of carnivores, and then drops away again. In the Triassic, for instance, there were four major families of herbivores, which diminished at the beginning of the Jurassic; at the end of the Jurassic there were nine herbivore families. Fully aquatic marine reptiles show a similar pattern. Diversity apparently increases as time goes on, as long as the environment provides the opportunities. Environments that remained unchanged – like fresh-water wetlands – do not show an increase in diversity: crocodiles and turtles never evolved a wide variety of species. So what happened to the environment to limit diversity, particularly at the end of the Cretaceous?

In a unified land-mass climatic change is simply not enough to explain these extinctions. As Bakker points out, there is always climatic change of some kind going on and if any stratum is analyzed closely enough, some evidence will be found for it (such changes are part of the reason for the existence of separate strata.) Sometimes this may produce local variations in the balance between the species or families but even at the end of the Cretaceous, when the climate was cooling down, the winters were still mild enough for crocodile-types to survive as far north as Saskatchewan. Anyway extinctions occurred in the hot dry, continental interiors (e.g. Mongolia) as well as in the wet interior of central North America.

About the only thing that does correlate well with the overall pattern of extinction is the sea-level. Major drops in the sea-level – regressions, as they are known – occurred between the Triassic and the Jurassic, between the Jurassic and Cretaceous and at the end of the Cretaceous. Since water acts as a buffer, or blanket against large changes of temperature, such regressions would go hand in hand with lower temperatures. But as we have seen, this in itself is not enough to explain extinctions. What other effects could have been associated with the regressions?

First let us look again at the machinery of speciation. Bakker suggests that species form more quickly where there are a wide variety of niches to accommodate them. A variety of niches is associated with the more complex habitats of continental interiors. Natural barriers of any kind tend to increase speciation. These barriers may be extremely subtle and need not be geographical – a particular food source is good enough, like that which interrelates eucalyptus trees and koala bears – but often the barriers are large ones like mountains and seas. These are associated with high sea-levels, or transgressions. Large scale transgression therefore, is a form of evolutionary pressure and should result in the formation of new species. When the seas retreat, speciation declines. It is in this process, Bakker suggests, that we should look for an explanation as to why no new species arose to replace those dinosaurian species that became extinct at the end of the Cretaceous.

The mechanism that he proposes draws on the now well established theory of continental drift. In brief the continental plates move as currents well up from the center of the earth, dividing at the surface and carrying the plates along on their backs. The lines along which currents hit the surface mark the boundaries between plates that are moving apart. As the rock rises from the interior of the earth, it creates a ridge that drifts away to left and right like a conveyor belt. The moving rock leaves behind a constantly replaced line of mountains known as a mid-oceanic ridge. For instance down the middle of the Atlantic is a line of mountains that divides the Americas from Europe and Africa. A fast rate of continental drift produces large mid-oceanic ridges. Since such ridges equal in bulk mountain ranges hundreds, perhaps thousands, of miles long, large ridges involve a considerable displacement of the ocean waters. It is the size of mid-oceanic ridges, therefore, that controls the sea-level. In periods of rapid continental drift, the seas are raised by several hundred feet, inundating vast continental areas, creating extensive continental shelves, thus providing a number of new shallow-water and coastal habitats.

Legends of Living Dinosaurs

As far as scientists are concerned, dinosaurs have been, without any shadow of doubt, extinct for at least 60 million years. Yet the reason for their final disappearance has still not been satisfactorily explained. Might there not somewhere, in some remote rain forest, be the odd dinosaurian species surviving? This suggestion has inspired at least one good tale (see page 175), and countless films. But there have also been some ostensibly factual reports, some of which have been gathered by Bernard Heuvelmans in his book *On the Track of Unknown Animals*.

Heuvelmans includes a London *Times* report, dated 17 November, 1919, of a certain Lepage, in charge of railway construction in the Belgian Congo, who was out hunting when 'he came upon an extraordinary monster, which charged at him. Lepage fired but was forced to flee, with the monster in chase. The animal before long gave up the chase and Lepage was able to examine it through his binoculars. The animal, he says, was about 24 feet in length with a long pointed snout adorned with tusks like horns and a short horn above the nostrils. The front feet were like those of a horse and the hind hoofs were cloven. There was a scaly hump on the monster's shoulder.' The description is reminiscent of a *Triceratops* (although *Triceratops* had horns, not tusks, and solid elephantine feet).

The report later became embellished in the media with reports of a living '*Brontosaurus*,' which were later discredited by a letter from a member of Washington's Smithsonian Institute who showed these reports to be pure rumors and hoaxes.

Then, in 1932, a young South African big-game hunter, F Grobler, reported a monstrous lizard which supposedly lived in the marshes where Zaire, Angola and Zambia now join. *The Rhodesian Herald* wrote: 'It is known by the native name of "Chepekwe." The natives in Central Africa used to call it the water lion. It can best be described as a huge leguan [iguana], the weight of which is estimated at about four tons or more.' Grobler claimed to have seen a photograph of the creature on top of a hippo it had killed. This report too was discredited by a later hoax perpetrated by a Swede, J C Johanson, whose supposed adventure with a 'Chepekwe' was reported in graphic detail in *The Rhodesian Herald*. Johanson said he saw a monster, about 16 yards in length, with a lizard's head and tail, which was 'tearing lumps from a dead rhino. It was covered in ooze . . . I could plainly hear the crunching of rhino bones in the lizard's mouth.' The report was accompanied by a blurry photograph of a monitor lizard superimposed on the carcass of a hippo or rhino.

Heuvelmans comments that when the rumors and hoaxes are removed there apparently remains a body of evidence not so easily dismissed. Large, apparently reptilian creatures have been reported by local tribes from an area 2000 miles across, which includes the upper reaches of the Congo, the Nile, and the Zambesi. Many reports, Heuvelmans concludes, can be attributed to pythons, crocodiles, fishes or lizards but there is a hard core of local folklore which apparently relates to an amphibious, hippo-sized creature with a long neck and a horn on its nose.

If it is there, what is it? 'In outline it is certainly like a dinosaur,' says Heuvelmans. *Which* dinosaur depends somewhat on the report. Sometimes it seems to be a ceratopsian (except that ceratopsians were vegetarian and their remains are not known in Africa). At other times, the supposed creature is more reminiscent of a small sauropod (but no sauropods were carnivorous). Anyway, it seems almost beyond the bounds of possibility that one single species, out of so many families of dinosaurs, should have survived. Certainly Heuvelmans does not accept the suggestion; he favors the idea of a giant monitor lizard but concludes: 'The animals we are concerned with . . . are, if not actual dinosaurs, large unknown reptiles extraordinarily like them.'

A Theory of Extinction

These diagrams suggest a theory of the extinction of the dinosaurs. They relate a slowing in the rate of continental drift to a drop in sea level, increasing cold, and, in particular, to the disappearance of the variety of landscapes in which the dinosaurs evolved and lived.

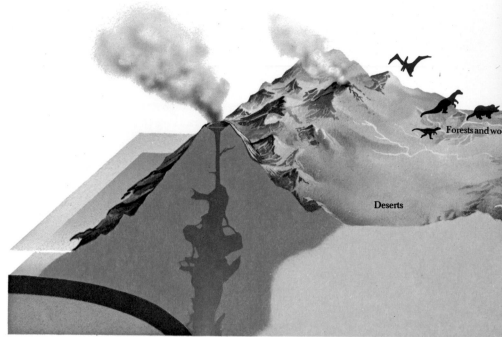

Forests and woo

Deserts

Subduction zone   Leading edge of continental plate: new mountains

In this generalized Cretaceous landscape, continental drift is seen proceeding at full pace. The mid-oceanic ridges (far right) are high as magma forces the continental plate away to the left. Where two plates meet, at left, the edge of the continent crumples into new mountains. Behind the mountains lie a wide diversity of habitats. The sea level is high and the continental shelf extends far from the coast, providing a shallow, warm environment for marine reptiles.

Deserts

Eroding mountains

Continental drift slows. The mid-oceanic ridges erode. The sea level begins to drop. At left, mountain building ceases and the mountains are reduced by erosion. Inland, the habitats that once provided self-contained niches for families of large dinosaurs begin to vanish.

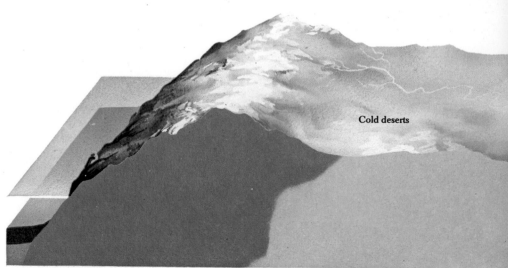

Cold deserts

Eroding mountains

With continental drift processes at a standstill, the mid-oceanic ridge has vanished. To take up the space, the sea has dropped away from the continental shelf. The shallow-water marine habitats have vanished, and along with them the marine reptiles. Inland, the landscape has become a uniform cold desert. Vegetation is sparse. Only small creatures – whether mammals, reptiles or birds – can exploit the now restricted habitats. The only surviving large creatures are the crocodiles and turtles whose habitats remain unchanged.

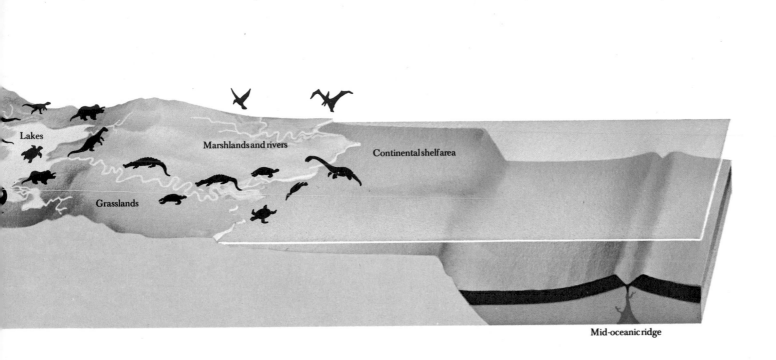

Lakes

Marshlands and rivers

Continental shelf area

Grasslands

Mid-oceanic ridge

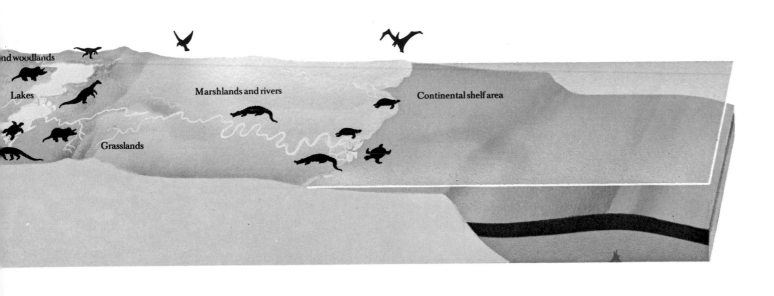

and woodlands

Lakes

Marshlands and rivers

Continental shelf area

Grasslands

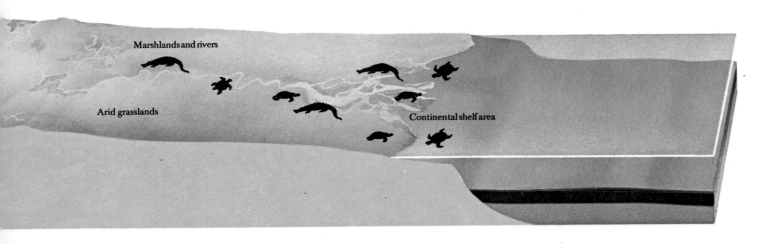

Marshlands and rivers

Arid grasslands

Continental shelf area

Another consequence of intensive continental drift is intensive mountain building. On the leading edges of the drifting plates, the earth crumples up into mountains. The effects of this process can be seen in the Alps (the result of Africa hitting Europe), in the Himalayas (the result of India floating across the Tethys Ocean and slamming into Asia), and in the Rocky Mountains and Andean ranges (formerly when South America was part of Africa the original Amazon had flowed to the west. When the South American plate ground up against the Pacific plate and threw up the Andes, the whole continent tilted and the Amazon began to flow the other way).

The mountains are constantly renewed under the influence of steady drift, a process that counteracts the effects of erosion and creates impenetrable barriers and a wide variety of climates. In combination with a high sea-level, the effect of rapid drift is to create the widest possible variety of niches, which can accommodate an ever changing array of species. Evolution proceeds, as it were, at full throttle. 'The high topographic-geographic diversity,' concludes Bakker, 'should give a high speciation rate and a high standing diversity within the continental highlands and adjacent plains. The pool of the potential immigrants to the lowland basins should be large. Immigration rates will be high.'

This argument has particular application to large animals like dinosaurs, for only when divided by large barriers can new species emerge. For a wide variety of dinosaur species to emerge, one condition would be a good supply of mountains, deserts, forests, rivers and lakes to keep them separate from each other. If this was not the case, incipient species would be in direct competition. Consequently a few species would spread in uniformity across all the world's land-masses. This in fact occurred earlier in the age of reptiles. Later as Pangaea broke up, species were additionally separated on their continental islands: hence the greater diversity of Late Cretaceous times. (By comparison, smaller creatures – like mammals – do not need such large barriers; their habitats are defined by small environments – a stream, a tree, a bush).

When continental drift slows, this whole extraordinary mechanism goes into reverse. The mid-oceanic ridges are no longer renewed by magma flowing up from below. The great chains of underwater mountains are worn away by the oceans. In the course of several million years, the ocean floor flattens out. No longer is there that great bulk of mountain to displace the waters of the oceans. To fill the gap, the waters retreat and sink away from the continental land masses. As the sea-level drops towards the edge of the continental shelves, huge plains formerly under water emerge, the great estuaries vanish, and areas previously divided by sea are joined together.

As the warming waters recede, the temperature drops and the tropical variety of plants begins to even out.

Meanwhile on the leading edges of the continental plates, mountains become old, erosion begins to wear away at the peaks, and after a few tens of millions of years, the jagged crests that typify new ranges like the Himalayas become no more than rounded hillocks like the Appalachians. Eventually the barriers that once powered the evolution of large species have vanished completely. In the lowlands and the coastal areas, of course, conditions have remained largely unchanged. They are still warm and wet as before but now those species that inhabit the coastal areas have no replacement when they become extinct. Quite rapidly in evolutionary terms, both herbivores and carnivores will vanish, leaving the world to those creatures small enough to be divided by the remaining barriers.

The correlation between regressions and extinctions suggest the solution to two of the minor problems: the survival of fresh-water aquatic species and the death of the large marine reptiles. Retreating seas do not affect the number of lakes and rivers. Higher lakes may dry up but lower ones are created, and rivers will always run down to the sea, however far away the sea is. Fresh water aquatic species, like crocodiles and turtles, will simply migrate with their habitats and remain unaffected by any of the extinctions. Secondly the regression of the seas towards the edge of the continental shelves, where the coastlines plunge into the oceanic depths, means that there are fewer shallow seas. This would impose a pressure on any species that could not adapt itself to deep-sea living. Such may well have been the case with the plesiosaurs. (The ichthyosaurs had vanished earlier in the Cretaceous for reasons that are simply not known.) Mosasaurs and sea-crocodiles could have been similarly affected.

There is one problem: why should not a few species remain to fill the few remaining niches? What killed the last few species of dinosaur? Bakker does not answer this question directly. 'I believe no special mechanism is required,' he says but suggests that the extinction was probably the cause of one of the agents traditionally mentioned as the one and only reason for the extinction of *all* dinosaurs – climatic change, floral change, parasites, or a combination of these. The most likely of these, he thinks, is the increasing cold. If at this stage the engine of evolution had been still highly tuned, no doubt dinosaurian species would have evolved that could have coped with the increasing cold. Bakker himself believes that in a way, they already *had* appeared: they were the birds, who had evolved their insulation in the form of feathers.

Bakker's suggestion is not of course a total answer. There are a number of vital questions that still demand detailed consideration. Does the sea-level in fact drop solely because continental drift slows (the mid-oceanic ridge may wear away but its bulk is merely distributed over the sea-bed, where it should still take up the same amount of space)? Do species in fact evolve in the 'continental' interiors. And why *did* the last surviving families die out, if there were still odd pockets in which they might have survived? Nevertheless, Bakker's approach – seeking to relate geology, biology and other comparable extinctions – will surely stimulate others to criticize, theorize, seek new evidence – and eventually perhaps to propose a watertight explanation of this fascinating problem.

With the disappearance of the dinosaurs, the world was left with no large animals. There were no creatures to graze the grasslands, or browse on the bushes, let alone the treetops. Hundreds of niches – even in an impoverished world – existed to be exploited, and there, lurking in burrows, scurrying between the roots of trees, and clinging to the branches in the upper levels of the forests were the creatures who would now inherit the earth: the mammals.

Bibliography

Bakker, R T, *Dinosaur Renaissance, Scientific American*, April, 1975

Charig, Alan & Horsfield, Brenda, *Before the Ark*. BBC, London, 1975

Colbert, Edwin H, *Dinosaurs: Their Discovery and their World*. Hutchinson, London, 1962

Colbert, Edwin H, *Evolution of the Vertebrates*. Second ed., Wiley, New York, 1969

Colbert, Edwin H, *Men and Dinosaurs: The Search in Field and Laboratory*. Penguin, 1971

Colbert, Edwin H, *The Age of Reptiles*. Weidenfeld & Nicolson, London, 1965

Colbert, Edwin H, *Wandering Lands and Animals*. Hutchinson, London, 1974

Desmond, A J, *The Hot-blooded Dinosaurs*. Hardback: Blond & Briggs, London, 1975; Paperback: Futura, 1977

Halstead, L B, *The Evolution and Ecology of Dinosaurs*. Eurobook, London, 1975

Halstead, L B, & Middleton, J A, *Bare Bones, an Exploration in Art and Science*. Oliver and Boyd, Edinburgh, 1972

Halstead, L B, *The Pattern of Vertebrate Evolution*. Oliver and Boyd, Edinburgh, 1969

Kielan-Jaworowska, Z, *Hunting for Dinosaurs*. MIT Press, Cambridge, Massachusetts, 1969

Kurten, B, *The Age of Dinosaurs*. Weidenfeld & Nicolson, London, 1968

Seeley, Harry Govier, *Dragons of the Air*. Hardback: Methuen, London, 1901; Paperback: Dover, 1967

Spinar, Z V and Burian, Z, *Life before Man*. Thames and Hudson, London, 1972

Stahl, Barbara J, *Vertebrate History: Problems in Evolution*. McGraw-Hill, New York, 1974

Swinton, W E, *Dinosaurs*. Fourth ed., British Museum (Natural History), 1969

Swinton, W E, *The Dinosaurs*. George Allen & Unwin Ltd, London; John Wiley & Sons Inc, New York, 1970

Time Life Books, *Life before Man*. Time-Life International, Amsterdam; Time-Life Books, New York

Tweedie, Michael, *The World of Dinosaurs*. Weidenfeld & Nicolson, London, 1977

Wendt, Herbert, *Before the Deluge*. Doubleday & Co, New York, 1968

Acknowledgements

Particular thanks go to Dr Alan Charig of the British Museum (Natural History) without whose encouragement and help this book would not have been possible; Dr Donald Baird of Princeton University; Joseph R Saulina of the American Museum of Natural History; Dr Richard Moody of the British Museum (Natural History); Phil Powell and the Oxford Museum; and Fleur Walsh

Artists

Richard Bell: *Frontispiece, 30–31, 94, 114–5, 134–4, 158–9, 170–1, 178–9,*

Linda Broad: *47, 50, 62, 63, 66–78, 70–71, 74, 77, 79, 82, 90, 98, 99, 100, 102, 110, 118, 122, 123, 139, 151, 154, 162, 163*

Gary Hinks: *54–55, 58–59, 86–87, 186–7*

Petula Stone: *91*

Photographs supplied by:

Heather Angel: Biofotos: *18, 46, 182*

Courtesy of the American Museum of Natural History: *26, 38, 39, 40, 80–1, 92, 137*

Dr Donald Baird: *Endpapers, 19, 27, (Photo: R W Seldan, R Bridenburgh), 34, 53, 60, 69, 82–83, 111, 123, 126, 127, 130, 146, 147, 150, 151, 166–7*

By kind permission of BBC Publications: *52*

By courtesy of the British Museum (Natural History): *16, 18, 21, 98, 100–1, 102, 113, 153*

Bruce Coleman Ltd: *147, 182–3 (Photos by Jane Burton, S C Bisserot, Frith & Frith)*

California Academy of Sciences: *8–9*

E H Colbert: *35, 41, 119*

Daily Telegraph Colour Library: *125*

Dan Freeman: *183*

Michael Freeman: *106–7*

Hayle Observatories: *177*

Illustrated London News: *64, 120–1, 128–9, 132–3, 164*

Imitor: *17, 19, 20, 23, 36, 37, 111, 116, 130*

Patrimonie de l'Institut Royal des Sciences Naturelles de Belgique: 28, 29

Institut und Museum für Geologie und Paläontologie der Universität, Tübingen, Photo:

Werner Wetzel: *73*

Professor Kielan-Jaworoska: *118, 138–9*

Mansell Collection: *25*

Mary Evans Picture Library: *24*

Mark Mason: Pronda Pronda (with thanks to the Oxford Museum): *21, 49, 63, 78, 93, 142–3*

By courtesy of the Museum für Naturkunde der Humboldt-Universität, DDR Berlin: *73, 85, 96–97, 103–5, 160–1*

Musée Nationale d'Histoire Naturelle, Institut de Paléontologie, Paris: *22*

National Museums of Canada: *41*

Popperfoto: *179*

Princeton University, Photo: Willard Starks: *6–7*

Punch: *36*

RIDA: *19, 55, 117 (Photo: P Whybrow)*

Sternberg Memorial Museum, Kansas: *155*

University of Michigan Museum of Paleontology, by courtesy of Professor R V Kesling: *146*

© Walt Disney Productions: *168*

Yale University Peabody Museum of Natural History: *112*

Index

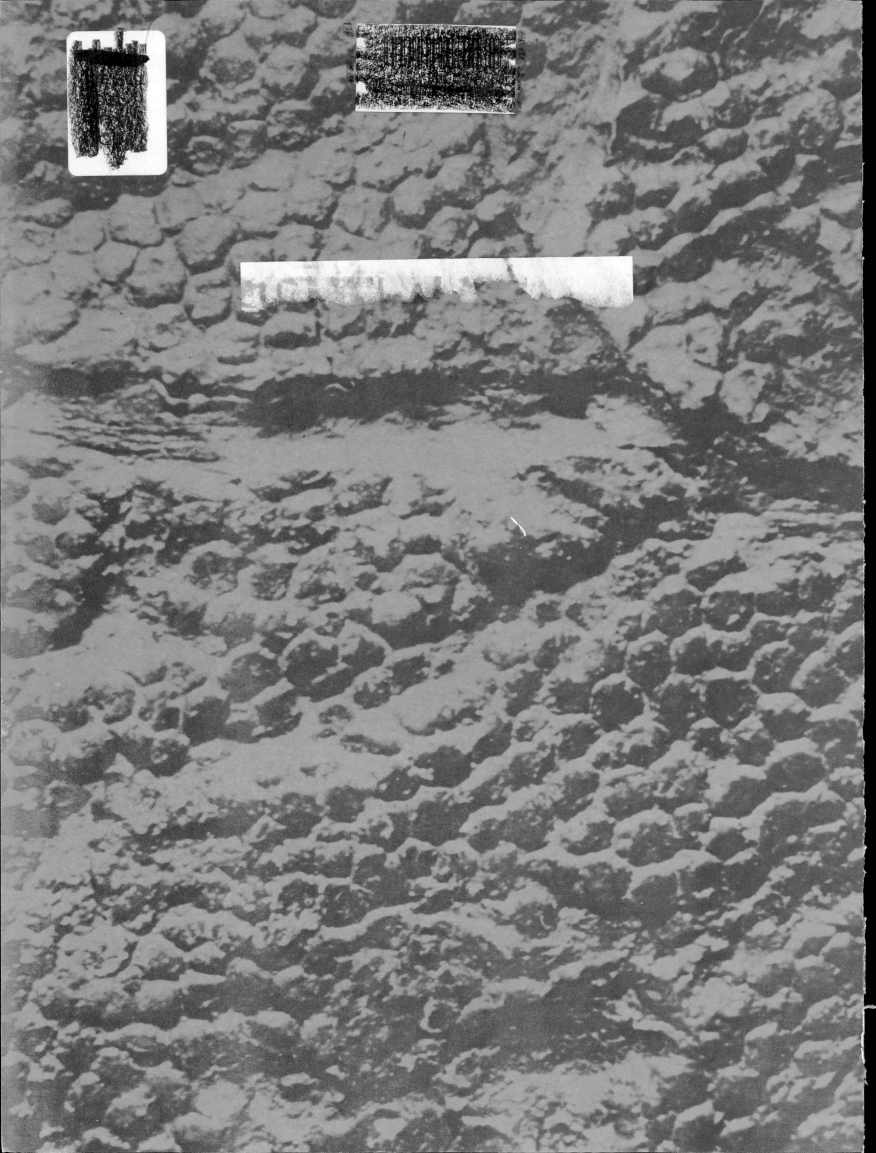